Ceramic Art of Southeast Asia

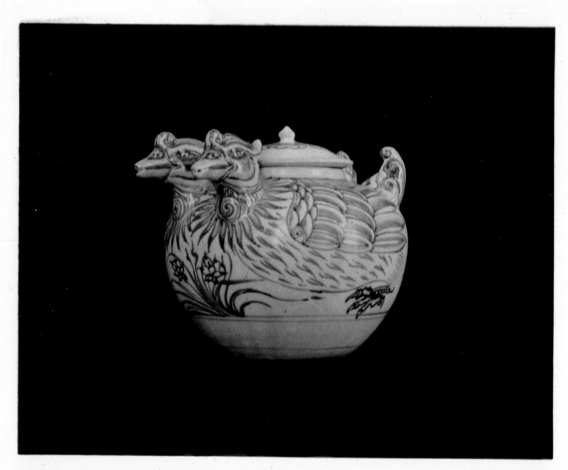

85

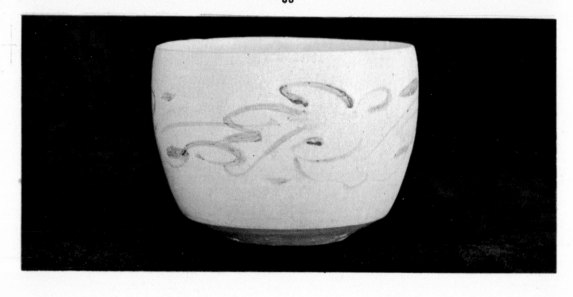

105

THE SOUTHEAST ASIAN CERAMIC SOCIETY

FIRST ANNUAL EXHIBITION

CERAMIC ART

OF

SOUTHEAST ASIA

INTRODUCTION AND DESCRIPTIVE NOTES

by

WILLIAM WILLETTS

THE ART MUSEUM

THE UNIVERSITY OF SINGAPORE

June-July 1971

INTRODUCTION

This that you see before you is the inaugural exhibition of the nascent South-east Asian Ceramic Society. The Society's stated aim being to promote appreciation and knowledge of the ceramic art of China and countries adjacent to China, especially those of Southeast Asia, we decided to start on our own doorstep and present an exhibition of Southeast Asian wares exclusively: that is to say, pottery of continental Southeast Asia exclusive of South China and Laos and of peninsular Thailand and Malaysia with Singapore. In effect this means the pottery of two main manufacturing regions, Thailand and Vietnam, with Cambodia, of lesser importance from a ceramic point of view, occupying a geographical position in between.

Most of the pots you now see on the Museum shelves were made either at the Sukhothai or Sawankoloke kilns of Thailand, or at kilns in the northern part of the old kingdom of Annam which to-day forms part of North Vietnam. The majority of pieces in both these groups belong either to the 14th or the 15th centuries, so that they are between five and six hundred years old. The earliest wares on display, on the other hand, are undoubtedly those here called 'Khmer', which date from the 10th to the 13th centuries, and which were made either in Cambodia or in Thai territory then under Cambodian control. The latest are wares from the northern Thai kilns at Sankampaeng and Kalong dating from the late 15th to 16th centuries.

* * *

It is now generally agreed that recent excavations of ancient burials in the Philippine Islands, initiated by Robert B. Fox in 1958 at Calatagan and continued by Mr. and Mrs. Locsin at Manila, have opened a new chapter in the history of Far Eastern ceramic art. The pots so brought to light may or may not have been put to brief domestic use by the islanders, but generally speaking another and somewhat *outré* destiny awaited them, one certainly undreamed of by their makers, namely to be buried as grave furniture with the dead.

* * *

In Singapore and its hinterland no such buried treasure probably awaits dis-covery. On the other hand, due to its favourable commercial and geographical situation, Singapore has since the end of 'confrontasi' been resorted to by a group of Indonesian pottery dealers, their wicker baskets filled to bursting with the ceramic yield of hundreds of more or less clandestine excavations of graves scattered all over the Indonesian Archipelago, but mainly in its eastern sector.

A year or so ago then (but now in a perceptibly diminished flow) large quantities of ceramic wares of some considerable antiquity, made originally in China and the above-mentioned countries of Southeast Asia, were arriving week by week in Singapore, the nearest suitable market outside Indonesia. Among them many were of excellent quality, and many of surpassing interest to ceramic historians on account of the unusual and indeed unrecorded features that they presented. The phenomenon quickly attracted the attention of local art collectors, and some who at the time were not, and as a result much fine pottery remained in Singapore that otherwise would have gone on to destinations such as Bangkok, Hong Kong, Japan, and America, and been permanently lost to the region. As local interest grew, so the Southeast Asian Ceramic Society came into being.

Almost all the pottery in this exhibition has lain for centuries undisturbed among the bones of Indonesian islanders. Now grinding economic necessity, plus an acute awareness among the Indonesians themselves of the commercial value these pots possess outside Indonesia, has forced them to the surface of the soil. Equally good collections could probably still be put together in the Philippines, though at a price. But ceramics recovered from Indonesia do not constitute precisely the same spectrum of pottery-types as we find in, say, the Locsin's book *Oriental Ceramics Discovered in the Philippines*, as is well understood. This may partly be due simply to a difference in the date of the interments. The graveyard at Santa Ana in Manila, as an example, seems to date mainly from a period somewhat earlier than most other burials with pots excavated in the Philippines, i.e. from the late 10th to the early 13th centuries; Sawankoloke wares, as we now understand the chronology, could not be expected to occur in such a context. Again it might be due to divergences in taste between islanders in the Indonesian and Philippine parts of the archipelago, or again to the pattern of trade established by merchants and shippers. In broad terms one may say that the proportion of Southeast Asian wares is significantly higher in Indonesia than in the Philippines; more Sawankoloke and Annamese pieces, and in much greater variety, seem to come from Indonesia than from the Philippines. Conversely, Philippine collections are far richer in early Chinese types than are those we possess here, got in the main from Indonesia. Yet both areas were included in what was essentially the same cultural vortex, the same movement of trade and commerce, and, with such exceptions as that noted above, the same period of time.

As might be predicated from what has just been said, the distribution of pottery-types is not uniform all over the Indonesian archipelago. Pots brought in from Acheh at the northwestern tip of Sumatra present a different appearence, when seen in constellation, from a collection made in Sulawesi, say, or West Irian in the extreme far east of the archipelago. Sulawesi, nearest geographically to the Philippine group, yields an almost identical range of buried imported ceramics. It includes for example 14th-century blue-and-white wares usually in the form of delicate little jarlets, related plain *ying-ch'ing* wares such as bottle-gourd ewers, and related iron-brown spotted wares; as also the early Tê-hua ware which the present writer calls 'Marco Polo', the true ancestor of the blanc-de-chines.

It is not practical, on the basis of available evidence, to plot the detailed distribution of imported ceramics throughout the Indonesian archipelago, and so perhaps arrive at an underlying meaning. The Indonesian disinterments are never properly documented, and the dealers make up their stocks piecemeal and often seem to have little or no idea as to the specific provenance of individual pieces. Very often they do know, of course, but are unwilling to say, and taking into account the secretive nature of the trade as well as the large sums of money involved this is very understandable. But the task of compiling a ceramic map of Indonesia could and should be undertaken.

*   *   *

The ceramic revival of the last few years, promoted by these excavations and pin-pointed by the symposium at Manila in 1968 to which ceramicists from all over the world were drawn, has also abundantly filled in the outline picture painted by Orsay de Flines in his *Gids voor de Keramische Versameling (Uitheemse Keramiek)*, the guide to the ceramic collection of the Batavia (Djakarta) Museum first published in 1949, in respect of antique pottery imported into Indonesia, and particularly of Annamese, Sawankoloke, and Sukhothai wares.

I say revival deliberately, because these pots with their fresh and vigorous air bestir the senses, and awaken sensibilities lulled almost into insensibility, it may be, by the still mathematical perfection of the Imperial Ming and 18th-century wares of which they are in their very essence the antithesis. I am glad that this should be so, for in my view adulation of ceramic perfection, and nothing short of perfection, inevitably leads to a serious loss in sensitivity towards much more ordinary sorts of pots. When the example is set by the wealthiest and most influential connoisseurs of ceramic art, the great collectors, a general perversion of taste is bound to ensue, giving rise to a conventional and ill-founded snobbery in respect of what may or may not be collected, so that the one commands a king's ransom and the other fails to fetch a market price at all. It would be silly to pretend that the Southeast Asian wares represent any particular consummation in the history of ceramic art. But the qualities they manifest are not skin deep, nor likely to prove transitory in their appeal. One may confidently say that this barely-known range of provincial pottery from the deep south of Asia will increasingly win the admiration of true lovers of pottery, because as pots they are good pots — some of them indeed totally convincing as ultimate artistic entities.

GROUP ONE. KHMER

The place of manufacture of at least some Khmer pottery, and perhaps most of it, is on the hill called Phnom Kulen 40 kilometres or so north-east of Angkor. The actual kiln-site is said to be a place by the name of Rong Chen, near the ruined temple Krus Prah Aram Rong Chen which lies some half a kilometre due south of Prasat Kaki on a dead straight line between it and Prasat Damrei Krap. No detailed examination of the site has been made, but it appears that manufacture continued over at least three centuries after the establishment of the Khmer dynasty at the Phnom Kulen by Jayavarman II in 802 A.D.

It would appear, moreover, as if the pottery can be classified chronologically into the following four groups:

1. *Kulen.* *10th century.* With a creamy-white or pale greenish celadon glaze. Cf. nos 13 and 18, and perhaps 17.

2. *Baphuon.* *11th century.* So-called 'deux couleurs'; the body being light and the glaze dark, or, apparently, *vice versa.*

3. *Angkor Wat.* *Early 12th century.* With the characteristic sooty dark-brown glaze on a dark biscuit. Cf. nos 1, 3, 4, 7.

4. *Bayon.* *Late 12th to early 13th century.* Described as having a very coarse body beneath a dark brown glaze. Cf. no 8.

These indications are, of course, ridiculously slight, but they should at least be sufficient to dispel a widespread belief that Khmer pottery was of necessity largely or wholly produced in Thailand, and that it was, at some degree in time removed, the direct ancestor of the Sawankoloke brown-glazed monochromes. I shall return to the latter question in particular when discussing the Sawankoloke kilns, but the question as to whether any Khmer wares at all were produced in Thailand, and if so where, is an insistent one. How does one explain the fact, for instance, that most Khmer pottery now on the market is to be found in Bangkok? Does this not argue the existence of Khmer kilns on Thai soil?

There is a considerable possibility that Khmer kilns lie in the vicinity of Surin and Srisaket, two towns situated some 40 miles north of the Cambodian border and about 100 and 115 miles north of Angkor respectively. Sherds recovered by Dr. and Mrs. Richard Lauriston Sharp have been identified by Monsieur Bernard Groslier as of the same type as the Phnom Kulen material. Moreover Mr. Dean Frasché has claimed that the distinctive deep hollow or "well" inside the base of some Khmer pots, e.g. nos 1, 2, and 5, is confined to the group supposed to have been manufactured on Thai territory. Once again the need for direct investigation becomes apparent.

Information regarding possible Khmer kilns in Thailand was kindly conveyed to me by the Vice-President of the Society. Monsieur Jacques Dumarçay of the École Française d'Extrême-Orient no less obligingly supplied the information regarding Khmer kilns on Phnom Kulen; in attributing dates to the present collection I have tentatively used the classification he outlined for my benefit.

* * *

Khmer wares show great internal consistency as a group. By this I mean that each and every individual piece shares certain strongly marked characteristics with other pieces, though not always in the same combinations, and these characteristics are manifest in pottery shape, paste, glaze, decoration and decorative technique, and potting technique. Moreover, when added up they amount to a distinctive total pottery form which is *sui generis* and quite unlike anything we associate with the

Chinese tradition.[1] In respect of form Khmer pottery is also sharply differentiated from that of Annam, Sukhothai, and Sawankoloke, all of which partake in some degree of the Chinese tradition.

Khmer pottery-shapes are unusual, sometimes fanciful. Theriomorphic additions are frequent. A flat gourd-like jar, e.g. no. 3 and no. 4, is typical. Decoration usually takes the form of circular bands upon the shoulder, interrupted with mechanical regularity by wedge-shaped incisions which were perhaps rouletted, or of raised or moulded bands, or other simple geometrical ornamentation. On the body, groups of parallel or somewhat converging vertical incised lines are typical.

The decoration is so precise, the vessel-shapes so taut, firm, and compact, that it is as though they were made of old, tooled leather. The impression is re-inforced by the sooty matt appearance of the glaze. This is typically dark chocolate-brown in colour, but there is also a dark olive-green variety, and another that looks like the Chinese 18th-century 'tea-dust' glaze, as well as the creamy-white or pale celadon glaze seemingly associated with the earliest period of Khmer pottery manufacture. The olive-green and pale celadon glazes, particularly, tend to be patchy and mottled. The Khmer paste is rough and poorly levigated, and contains so much iron that the visible biscuit is often charcoal-black in colour after oxidation.

The foot is absolutely diagnostic. It is never carved out to leave a footrim (though sometimes bounded by a raised ridge), but is often button-shaped, and the base is often slightly concave. The foot as a whole has a rough-and-ready appearence. Concentric grooves made by the cord that cut the pot off the wheel, and looking like thumb-prints, add to the impression of a hasty and summary potting practice.

The group as a whole has an air of latency or withdrawal, and the pots are as though they were asleep. These are qualities which we associate, too, with early Khmer and even pre-Khmer monumental and decorative sculptures and bas-reliefs.

GROUP TWO. ANNAMESE

The territory to which the term 'Annamese' here refers is that part of North Vietnam lying within one or two hundred kilometres' radius of the capital at Hanoi. This region, known by the Vietnamese themselves by various names such as Dai Viet

---

1. It is worth making this point since some French archaeologists, including Aymonier and Georges Groslier, have assumed that the Khmer glazed stoneware manufacture was inaugurated and subsequently supervised by Chinese potters. In 1921 Groslier made this claim when referring to the existence of large heaps of sherds of glazed pottery tiles and vessels at Sampon Thieu, a place about 2 kilometres S.S.W. of Anglong Thom on Phnom Kulen (and so about the same distance S.S.E. of Rong Chen); but he added that stylistically the products are in every respect Khmer, classical and distinctive, and with this opinion the present writer agrees. In view of the established strength of the Chinese ceramic tradition, it is difficult to believe that an overt Chinese influence would not be evident in classical Khmer pottery had the potters been Chinese.

and Dai Nam, but never by the pejorative Chinese term Annam, "pacified south", came under French control at the beginning of the 19th century, and was then known to Europeans as Tongking, while Annam was the name given to the long coastal strip lying immediately to its south. The king of the combined territories of Tongking and Annam ruled at Hué.

Hanoi, nevertheless, was the traditional capital of the kings of Annam, firstly for a period of 400 years between 1009 and 1400, then, after a short period of Chinese occupation, from 1428 up to the coming of the French. It would be reasonable to surmise that the Annamese kilns were located not far from the capital, and this supposition hardens to a virtual certainty when we take into account the existence of abundant deposits of kaolin and feldspar near at hand — feldspar at Thanh-hoa 175 kilometres south of Hanoi, and kaolin and feldspar at Dong-trieu, 52 kilometres east of Hanoi on the road to Haiphong.

There are in fact three major pottery factories inside the area, operational at least until a few years ago. A large variety of domestic wares for local consumption is or was made at Huong-canh, which is 47½ kilometres north-west of Hanoi on the road to Viet-tri. The pottery village of Tho-ha, lying at a distance of 4 kilometres from the provincial capital of Bac-ninh, itself 30 kilometres north-east of Hanoi, is probably of greater historical signifance. The factory is said to have been established in 1465 by a potter coming from Lau-khé in Hai-duong province, some 60 kilometres east of Hanoi on the Red River. According to legend Lau-khé was where the first continental Chinese potter, Hoang Quang Hung, settled in the 3rd century B.C. and thereby instituted the potter's craft in Annam. A temple at Tho-ha is dedicated to Hoang Quang Hung, and also to Truong Trung Ai, the alleged first Annamese potter at Lau-khé.

The third important pottery centre is Bat-trang, meaning literally "pottery factory". This town lies some 10 kilometres due south of Hanoi, on the Red River and the road to Ninh-binh and Thanh-hoa. It is said to have been founded between 1527 and 1533 by potters from Bo-bat, a village in Ninh-binh or Thanh-hoa province, and seems to have been in continuous production since that time. In the twenties of this century its population is said to have numbered 4,000, all concerned directly or indirectly in the manufacture of pottery and porcelain. The kaolin was brought from Dong-trieu, and the feldspar from Thanh-hoa, and the stacks of wood firing for the kilns were conspicuous on the skyline long before the town itself came into view. It might well be called the Ching-tê-chên of Annam; indeed the *Guide Madrolle* observes that most of its manufacturing processess and techniques were adopted from that centre.

Now if it is true that Bat-trang was founded in the mid-16th century, then it cannot of course have been the production-centre for the 15th- and possibly late 14th-century Annamese blue-and-white, the most important single group of Annamese wares. On the other hand Bat-trang may well have begotten such ultra-fine porcelains as nos 82 and 85, which in ceramic quality match the very best wares of the Ming dynasty. Perhaps therefore pots such as these might be dated to the 16th century, a supposition supported by the evidence of their forms.

We shall see when describing no 93 that in the 17th century Bat-trang was the centre for the manufacture of large blue-and-white baluster vases used as altar-pieces. In his monograph on Annamese 'chocolate bases' (bases chocolatées) d'Argencé mentions a Bat-trang piece dated to the year 1625, without further reference.

There is I believe no evidence to show that either of the other two recently surviving factories were operating in the 14th or 15th centuries, though Tho-ha is one of a short list of places at which according to Okuda French archaeologists have reported kiln-sites, presumably ancient. Since tradition links Tho-ha with an earlier factory at Lau-khé in Hai-duong, and Bat-trang with Bo-bat, these localities would certainly be worth investigating. Indeed this may already have been done.

$$* \qquad * \qquad *$$

The period of Chinese occupation from 1400 to 1428 was probably crucial in the development of Annamese ceramics. For with Chinese political ascendancy, a way was opened for the penetration of Chinese ceramic styles and fashions into Annam. It is of course precisely in the Chinese blue-and-white ware of the latter half of the 14th century that we find the source of inspiration for the main Annamese blue-and-white oeuvre.

The blue-and-whites, and the closely related blue-and-white wares with on-glaze enamel decoration, are in general all that the ceramic world knows or understands by the term 'Annamese'. The only considerable book to have been published on the subject, or at least to have enjoyed currency in Western ceramic circles, is Okuda Seichii's Annamese Ceramics, Tokyo 1954. It is obvious at first perusal of this book that fully half the wares illustrated therein are not Annamese at all, but south Chinese.[2] But when all these ceramic strays, such as south Chinese celadons, early Tê-hua types, Ming bazaar blue-and-whites, Swatow enamelled dishes, Shekwan wares, and so forth have been rounded up, there still remain a minority (I make it 36 out of 76 vessels illustrated) all patently members of the same family-clan, united by certain physical characteristics (such as the 'chocolate base') which ceramic historians generally have come to accept as 'Annamese'.

In fact seven families of Annamese wares may be discriminated by virtue of differences in mode of decoration and type of glaze, as follows:

1. Wares decorated in underglaze blue.

2. Wares enamelled in dark tomato-red on the biscuit.

3. Wares decorated in underglaze blue, with on-glaze tomato-red and leaf-green enamels.

---

2. The point is also made by d'Argencé: "...il est déjà bien certain que bon nombre de pièces présentées par M. Okuda comme spécifiquement 'annamites'...devront être reversées au fonds chinois." He notes that Mlle Madeleine David is of the same opinion.

4. Wares decorated in underglaze iron-b'ack.

5. Cream-glazed monochrome wares.

6. Green-glazed monochrome wares.

7. Brown-glazed monochrome wares.

The technical characteristics of these seven families are described more particularly in the notes. As to the distribution of vessel-types within the families, the blue-and-whites include among them large offering-dishes with or without scalloped edges, similar dishes but of medium size, large *yü hu ch'un p'ing* vases, *mei p'ing* vases, outsize baluster vases for altars, open bowls with everted mouthrims, covered bowls (*po kang*), miniature amphorae, miniature jars with moulded sides, circular covered boxes, covered boxes in the shape of crabs, ewers, kendis, water droppers, covered potiches partly modelled in the shape of gallinaceous or water birds, small globular jars with or without ring-handles, and ceramic figurines. In general the blue-and-whites are anchored firmly within the classical Chinese repertory of vessel-shapes.

Among the underglaze iron-black wares shapes are more original, as indeed is the case with the three monochrome ranges. And in this connection I am bound to disagree with Messrs Koyama and Figgess, who say more than once in the section devoted to Annamese wares in their book *Two Thousand Years of Oriental Ceramics,* London 1961, that Annamese potters were at all times under Chinese influence. Foremost among vessels decorated in underglaze iron-black is the beaker (cf. nos. 101, 103, 104 and 105), a clean, pure ceramic shape given definitive form by the Annamese potter. Also conspicuous are dishes and bowls with floral sprays as centre medallions, and there is a *yü hu ch'un p'ing* vase.

Among the infrequent cream-glazed monochromes are small crucible-shaped bowls, shallow bowls with S-shaped profiles, jarlets, and beakers as in the previous category. The apple-green copper-glazed wares include a delicious little cup-like bowl with vertical ribs on its outside wall, a miniature jar with moulded sides (found also among the blue-and-whites), a flat, circular covered box, a saucer-dish usually with a biscuited ring surrounding the centre medallion, and the beaker seen in the iron-black range. There are also (though we have none to show) superb covered boxes sculpted in the shape of crabs.

The brown-glazed monochromes include beakers, saucer-dishes, bowls, *yü hu ch'un p'ing* vases, and water droppers; but the true provenance of some members of these last two groups is perhaps less certain.

The *matière* of all these pots is a fine, smooth, homogeneous, putty-coloured paste usually visible on the footrim and the bottom of the foot, or base. The foot is sometimes flat, without a footrim; but a footrim is normally provided, high in the case of bowls, but more usually wide and shallow, the base being recessed no more than a millimetre or so.

The footrim is nearly always neatly and carefully carved out, the outer side chamfered at its junction with the under side, and the inner side at its junction with the base. The whole foot was often left in biscuit; but in the case of bowls, and large- and medium-size offering-dishes, the inner side of the footrim and the entire base were as a rule coated with a slip or glaze, often applied while the pot was on the wheel (and so showing signs of the spiral motion), but sometimes apparently painted on afterwards. The slip is invariably chocolate-brown (*chocolatée*), the glaze usually oatmeal- or gum-coloured.

Beakers in the underglaze iron-black and cream-glazed ranges, though quite deep, appear to have been fired in stacks, one inside another, and separated from each other by disc pontils having 5 spurs; 5 spur-marks are invariably to be seen embedded in the glaze in the inside bottom of such a pot. There is here perhaps evidence of some sort of connection with Sukhothai, where precisely this sort of pontil was employed, as we shall see. Flat dishes and bowls with everted mouthrims were similarly fired in both ranges.

In the green and brown monochrome ranges a biscuited ring very often appears on the inside base of bowls and beakers. Its presence suggests a mode of firing in which vessels were placed in stacks. In the case of some bowls (e.g. nos. 133 and 146) one gets the distinct impression that the ring was cut down through the glaze *after firing*, in which case we may well conclude that the object was to remove the spur-marks embedded in the glaze. But in most specimens the ring seems never to have been glazed, but to have been fired in biscuit. In none is there any visible indication as to how the ring was used for firing.

One underglaze-blue dish (no. 88), similar in decorative form to bowls in underglaze iron-black, and I believe coeval with that group, shows a ring of six spur-marks embedded in the glaze round the centre medallion. But as far as the rest of the blue-and-whites are concerned I have been able to find no clue as to how they were fired, since there are no visible traces, and suppose that the technique whatever it was came directly from the Chinese potters' *vade mecum*. By comparison the firing techniques used in the other Annamese groups would seem to be primitive, which perhaps tends to bear out the present writer's impression that these groups are in fact earlier in date than the blue-and-whites, more distinctively Annamese, and in some manner connected with the Thai production. In particular the shape of the beakers, nos 101, 103, 104 and 105, seems to me wholly Annamese in inspiration and of the highest possible ceramic distinction.

I have referred to a possible connection between Annamese and Sukhothai pottery traditions, manifest perhaps in their common use of the disc pontil. The relationship becomes demonstrable in my view when we compare certain decorative motives, and the manner of their organisation, found on pots from both areas. Local collectors here well know how easy it is to mistake one for the other, until the essential criteria that separate them are taken into account. The resemblance between no. 148 (which is Sukhothai) and no. 88 (which is Annamese) involves the decoration on the flattened lip (a deteriorated classic scroll) and on the centre medallion. This latter shows a floral spray, summarily drawn. It may be compared with those featured on nos. 108 and 109, which are Annamese, particularly in respect of the curled leaves or leaf-tips. Another example is illustrated in *Ram*, pl. 31a, showing a Sukhothai sherd with a centre medallion floral spray, the leaves curled at their tips in Annamese fashion; pl. 31b shows a Sawankoloke version on a Sawankoloke sherd. Again, the fragmented curvilinear scroll on the outside wall of no. 148, similar to that on no. 157 (also Sukhothai), bears comparison with the abstract calligraphic scrolls on the outside walls of nos 108, 109, and 110 (all Annamese), as well as that of the underglaze blue example, no. 89 (also Annamese). No. 148 was intentionally put among the Annamese wares on exhibition in order to invite the comparison; but the present writer must confess that when an exhibitor pointed out that it was a Sukhothai piece, and therefore in the wrong bay-case, he forgot for a moment what it was doing there, and agreed that a mistake in identification had really been made.

If we admit the existence of the relationship, then we must ask the question: which tradition influenced which? Bearing in mind the fact that Sukhothai was already established by the year 1300 and had but a short lease of life, and that the main Annamese blue-and-white series began no earlier than the end of the 14th or beginning of the 15th century, then if the other Annamese groups are contemporary with the blue-and-whites, Sukhothai must clearly have influenced Annam. But taking into account the rudimentary state of Sukhothai ceramic technology, which we shall, the opposite would seem more likely to have been the case. The present writer believes that the Annamese underglaze iron-black wares, together with the copper-green, cream, and brown monochromes, and a very few pieces decorated in underglaze blue, such as nos 88 and 89, belong to an older phase in the Annamese output than the main group of blue-and-whites, which they antedate perhaps by as much as a century; and that generally speaking they were discontinued as soon as the latter made its dominating presence felt.

*   *   *

It may be observed that the character and disposition of the decoration on the inside walls of nos. 108, 109, and 110 suggests a relationship with early Chinese blue-and-white stem-cups of *shu fu* type such as *Philadelphia*, no. 4 (Junkunc), and no. 6 (Loo). These are generally ascribed to the 14th century but may well belong to the second half of the 13th.

Moreover the interior motive of no. 89, stylised though it is, is I believe sufficiently close in its general sense to those of *Philadelphia*, no. 5 (Pope), and no. 7 (Loo), as well as to *Stockholm*, nos. 1 and 2 (both Lindberg), to illustrate a genuine connection with this same Chinese group. The abstract calligraphic scroll on the outside wall of this blue-and-white bowl, on the other hand, is of the type found in the same position on the Annamese iron-black range of which nos. 108, 109 and 110 are typical examples; thus its apparent relationship with both groups would appear to confirm their relationship with each other. Granted a date in the late 13th or early 14th century for the Chinese blue-and-whites, then the Annamese iron-blacks must on this basis be their near contemporaries.

14

GROUPS THREE AND FOUR.   SUKHOTHAI AND SAWANKOLOKE

The first Thai kingdom of Sukhothai was founded soon after the death of Jayavarman VII in Cambodia (r. about 1181-1220), and during the reign of his successor Indravarman II.   The first Thai king was Bang Glang Tao, who inherited the title of Sri Indraditya that had originally been given to P'a Muang, his comrade-in-arms against the Khmer, by the Khmer ruler himself.   The second king of Sukhothai, Ban Muang, ruled between about 1250 and 1275, and the third was Ram Kamhaeng, the greatest in the line of Sukhothai rulers, who may have died either about 1299 or 1316.

The founding of the Sukhothai kingdom brought to an end Khmer rule in the province.   This is thought to have been at Chalieng in the great hairpin bend of the Yom River, some 55 kilometres north of Sukhothai and 3 kilometres south of the site of the new city of Sri Satchanalai, Sukhothai's twin.   Possibly stonewares had been produced at Chalieng (or rather not at Chalieng itself but at the Ban Ko Noi kilns about 14 kilometres upstream from Chalieng) during the period of Khmer occupation, that is to say in the 11th, 12th and early 13th centuries.   But the hypothesis stands in need of proof.   It has become the custom to call the brown-glazed stonewares made at Ban Ko Noi 'Chalieng', though with doubtful justification.   One supporting view is that since the wares in question are allegedly related to the brown-glazed wares called 'Khmer', then the former, or some of them, may very well date from the Khmer period, when Chalieng was also the seat of Khmer rule.   But wherein lies this alleged relationship?   'Chalieng' wares are brown-glazed, but it is not the same type of glaze as that found on the Khmer pots.   And otherwise?   The present writer cannot think of a single point of resemblance between the two groups — whether in respect of form-language in general, or of specific types or shapes of vessel, or of potting technique (in particular of the treatment of the foot).   In these respects, so fundamental in all pottery traditions, 'Chalieng' wares are at one with the other four families of the Sawankoloke group, by which name they should for preference be called.[3]

Thus the large globular ring-handled jars disrespectfully called 'coconuts' by the Indonesian dealers, and the much smaller narrow vessels, more like vials, that Spinks suggests may have been containers for oil or condiments, were produced in identical form in both the brown-glazed and the Sawankoloke celadon lines; so too were the miniature gourd-shaped vessels (hu lu p'ing).   The depressed globular covered potiche is found not only among the brown-glazed wares but also in both the underglaze iron-black and the pearly-white-glazed ranges.   So also is the covered box, which appears again as the commonest vessel-type in the range of incised biscuited

3.   I should explain that Sawankoloke (Sanscrit Svargaloka, 'The Place of Heaven') was the name given to Sri Satchanalai in the Ayuthya chronicles after the incorporation of Sukhothai into the Ayuthya kingdom in the 15th century.   The modern town of Sawankoloke is some distance away from the historical site.   It is a source of confusion that three places, Chalieng, Sir Satchanalai and Sawankoloke, should be contending for the privilege of lending their names to the ware made at the Ban Ko Noi factory between the end of the 13th and the middle of the 15th centuries.

wares. Large pear-shaped bottles (yü hu ch'un p'ing) with cup-shaped mouth occur in all five families. Indeed there is not a single vessel-type characteristic of the brown-glazed wares that is not represented in at least one of the other four families.

It is clear that the 'Chalieng' stonewares, as we know them, belong with the other Sawankoloke families and are their contemporaries, and have only the most tenuous connection, if that, with the earlier group we know as 'Khmer'.

*   *   *

The historical facts and legends relevant to the founding of the Thai stoneware potteries have been set out by Charles Spinks in his book *The Ceramic Wares of Siam*, so need not be re-stated here. As to whether Chinese potters actually accompanied the returning Thai diplomatic missions of the 1290's, this, as Spinks says, will probably never be known. Yet certain it is that within that decade or the next Chinese ceramic artists, artisans, and technicians began to arrive in Thailand and to set up factories there. The result was an unprecedented burst of ceramic creativity and output, first at Sukhothai, then, after a more or less brief interval, at Sawankoloke.

It is possible that production at Sukhothai had begun long before the first Thai diplomatic missions were sent to China. Yet taking into account the Chinese quality immediately apparent in the Sukhothai oeuvre, and the absence of any obvious fore-runner on Thai soil, the conclusion must be that Sukhothai began to produce about 1300, and not before. By the same token it has been argued that Sukhothai con-tinued long into the 14th and even 15th century, and indeed that it remained operative during the whole 150 years of the Sawankoloke factory.

We do not know exactly when production started at Sawankoloke, but what seems perfectly clear is that it was a second band of Chinese potters, coming from a different region of China, and heirs to a different local tradition, who settled at Sawankoloke. As is generally agreed, Sukhothai reflects the style and idiom of the Tzŭ Chou potteries of Hopei province of north China; whereas Sawankoloke is un-doubtedly the offspring of the great celadon factories of Chekiang.

Bearing in mind the poor technical quality of the Sukhothai wares due to quite abominably bad raw materials, and the comparative excellence of those of Sawan-koloke, one must surely conclude that Sukhothai preceded Sawankoloke, perhaps by a few decades. One is also surely justified in inferring that as soon as large-scale production got under way at Sawankoloke the Sukhothai factory was allowed to run down, and that it did so fairly quickly. Both were presumably under some central government authority in charge of production; being so close together, what would have been the object of keeping them both going, especially since one was so obviously technically inferior to the other?

There is another circumstance in support of the view that production at Suk-hothai was fairly short-lived, namely the comparative scarcity of Sukhothai wares compared with those of Sawankoloke in the dealers' samples. I would say the proportion was no higher than one to twenty. If it is argued that production at Sawan-koloke was on a much bigger scale, with more kilns, operatives, and so on, then my reply is that on an absolute numerical basis there are still not many Sukhothai pots to be found. The present writer has observed perhaps fewer than a hundred, from among all the wares he has seen come out of Indonesia, which must surely represent a perceptible fraction of the total number that originally went in.

It is possible to isolate and identify a group of Sawankoloke underglaze iron-black painted bowls, as well as some vases, bottles and kendis (e.g. nos 172-182), that are intermediate in decorative form between the familiar Sukhothai painted slipwares and the famous underglaze iron-black covered boxes and other well-known Sawankoloke lines. These could well have been made during a comparatively short period when the two factories were in simultaneous production. In other words, Sawankoloke seemingly made a conscious effort to assimilate the special expertise of the Sukhothai potters before the latter stopped potting, so that nothing of value should be lost to the new, booming industry. In fact, of course, vessels of this transitional group altogether lack the spontaneous and instinctual qualities we see in Sukhothai, and the delightful graphic freedom of Sukhothai is never afterwards reproduced in Thai ceramics, whether at Sawankoloke or the later kilns.

*   *   *

Turning now to the Sukhothai group specifically, we find that the body, paste or *matière* is a coarse, impure, poorly levigated kaolin which fires a dark brown, and in which can be seen an abundance of whitish particles scattered evenly through the matrix. One comes to regard this paste as absolutely distinctive of Sukhothai; so much so, in fact, that no. 172, which appears to exhibit it, is only with some mis-giving here identified as Sawankoloke.

The number of Sukhothai vessel-types is limited. Dishes, flat conical bowls, deep covered bowls, and *yü hu ch'un p'ing* bottles are practically all there are. There is nothing like the range, variety, or inventiveness that greets us when we enter the Sawankoloke showroom. Nor was the potting-technique in the least enterprising. The dirty body was invariably covered with a cream-coloured slip, on which decoration was applied with the brush dipped in an iron-black solution. But as a rule the slip does not extend to the lower outside body or the foot, whereby the characteristic fired biscuit lies exposed. The glaze has usually proved unstable, liable to degrada-tion, and in many cases has disappeared altogether, leaving behind a denuded and oddly unprotected-looking painted slipware surface. Moreover pots were very apt to suffer distortion during firing. Bottles and vases sag, the walls of dishes are prone to warp and twist, and to flop dangerously downwards to the level of the foot. And I am not referring here to kiln-wasters, but to pots that were actually sold, and sent overseas. The firing technique was deplorable, though admittedly the poor materials gave kiln operators no great encouragement to develop their skills. Again the foot, although allowed a carved footrim, was very roughly treated.

The decoration on the other hand is usually, though not invariably, vivid and convincing. Its quality is well illustrated by the fish medallion, the most frequent decorative motive of the group. Looking at these slight sketches, so tense, so full of life, so nimbly drawn, one is almost bound to feel that only a Chinese could have done them, so redolent are they, as Spinks says, of the laconic statements of the Ch'an Buddhist masters of the Sung.

Dishes and bowls, the most characteristic Sukhothai vessel-types, were fired in short stacks, each pot separated from the one above by a disc-shaped pontil having 5 short triangular spurs projecting from its under side like studs on the sole of a football boot. These spurs rested on or near the perimeter of the centre medallion of the pot below; in the case of the fish dishes, the marks they made are often well concealed among the brown-pigmented spots that usually cover the fishes' bodies. The pot above rested on its footrim upon the plain upper surface of the pontil.

The lowest member of the stack stood (or at least sometimes stood) on a *tubular pontil,* as no. 168 makes abundantly clear; the circular pontil scar on the base is unmistakeable, in every respect resembling the typical Sawankoloke scar. This bowl, then, *must* have been fired in an upright position, not inverted; Le May's erroneous explanation as to how the Sukhothai wares were stacked predicates, as Spinks rightly points out, that they were fired upside-down. But, in addition, the marks of five spurs can also be seen on the inside medallion of no. 168, showing where a disc pontil had rested during firing. Why should a disc pontil have been placed inside this bowl except to support a second bowl above it? And if a second, then a third. And so we have the beginning of a stack. No. 168 thus answers the question, left unanswered by Spinks in his discussion of the Sukhothai potting-technique (*Spinks II*, pp. 18-21), as to how the bottom pot in the stack was fired, and confirms that the stack was fired upright.

In the descriptive notes which follow I have drawn attention to examples of pots which seem to me to reflect the influence of Annam on Sukhothai (if not the other way around), as also to others with features later adopted by the potters of Sawankoloke. No 149 is a particularly interesting case, since on the one hand its source of inspiration might seem to be a Chinese Chi Chou *temmoku* type, of which I have cited an example, while on the other hand the 'sun-burst' motive seems to have passed from it (and others like it) into the Sawankoloke repertory as seen in no. 177.

*   *   *

The Sawankoloke tradition is from the ceramic point of view far superior to that of Sukhothai. To begin with, we have no fewer than five different families of Sawankoloke wares, those I have already named as underglaze iron-black wares, brown-glazed monochromes, pearly-white-glazed monochromes, incised biscuited wares, and celadons, and undoubtedly the celadons make the bravest showing. In the celadon range we find large and medium-sized offering dishes with plain or scalloped edges, either plain, or with incised ornament; similarly decorated large bowls, followed by a long series of bowls of various sizes, coming right down to small cup-like bowls often decorated with delicately gouged vertical striations on the outside wall; large and gracefully shaped potiches with covers, and large deep bowl-shaped covered jars; stem dishes (or what Spinks calls offering trays); kendis and water droppers, usually with the modelled head and tail of some water-bird; miniature flat, domed, brush pots or perhaps oil jars; large globular bottles, with or without ring-handles; smaller, less rotund bottles; yet smaller narrow bottles, or vials, with or without vertical gouged striations; miniature bottles; figurines, usually of the mother-and-child variety; vases, usually of *yü hu ch'un p'ing* type and with cup-shaped mouth; and miniature bottle-shaped vessels. The only outstanding types not found among the celadons are flattened globular covered potiches with ring-handles and circular covered boxes — as though the manufacture of these in celadon had for some reason been prohibited.

Among the other four Sawankoloke families far fewer shapes are to be found. The pearly-white-glazed wares comprise *yü hu ch'un p'ing* vases with cup-shaped mouths, bottle-gourd vessels, deep round lidded bowls, short straight-sided bowls (*lien tzŭ*), and covered potiches with or without ring-handles. The incised biscuited wares, often illuminated with pearly-white glaze or caramel-coloured slip, include tall jarlets, circular covered boxes, kendis, ewers, and a few figurines. The brown-glazed monochromes include *yü hu ch'un p'ing* vases, miniature gourd-shaped vessels, covered potiches with ring handles, covered boxes, and some figurines and ceramic sculptures, but little else. The underglaze iron-black wares include bowls, *yü hu ch'un p'ing* vases, bottles and small kendis with cup-shaped mouths, larger kendis, covered potiches, ceramic statuary, and a vast number of circular covered boxes.

The Sawankoloke *matière* is dense, heavy, resounding, well levigated, and relatively free from mineral impurities. Pots were fired by being placed, somewhat precariously, on the heads of hollow tubular pontils made of highly refractory clay and set in the sandy floor of the kiln, so that a full kiln must have looked like a bed of giant mushrooms or a cabbage patch. The tubular pontil, with the observed exception (cf. no. 168), is to the present writer's knowledge unique and distinctive of Sawankoloke, not known to occur elsewhere. Whether it was a Sawankoloke invention is perhaps less certain.

The circular scar left behind is diagnostic, and it tells us that the wares were fired in a reducing atmosphere, with carbon monoxide filling the kiln, and were later allowed to cool in the presence of oxygen when the kiln was opened and air let in. Within the cavity of the pontil, where oxygen could not easily get, the biscuit typically appears grey, indicating reduction, but on the exposed parts of the foot where oxygen could circulate freely the biscuit has flashed to its characteristic rust-red tint.

Again, Spinks supposes (*Spinks II*, p. 18, ftn. 2) that the black material of the scar is perhaps carbonised resin or pitch used as an adhesive to fix the pot as securely as might be on the head of the pontil. It is significant, therefore, that on pieces where the scar appear incomplete, that is to say where the seal would have been faulty, so that air could pass freely into the interior of the pontil, there is no difference in colour between that part of the base enclosed, and that not enclosed, by the pontil.

As well as the applied glaze, biscuited parts of the pot frequently appear as it were burnished or polished, indicating where wood ash had fallen onto the surface during firing and, acting as a flux, converted a thin outer layer of biscuit into a natural glaze. Once again, no such glaze ever appears inside the pontil scar, where the biscuit was protected from wood ash floating in the kiln atmosphere.

GROUP FIVE. SANKAMPAENG AND KALONG

The pottery site known by the name of Sankampaeng in northern Thailand was discovered by Kraisri Nimmanahaeminda in 1952. It is in the Sankampaeng district of Chiengmai province, a mile or so beyond the village of Ontai, itself about 15 miles to the southeast of Chiengmai in the direction of Lamp'un. The kilns, of which 83 have so far been discovered, are in the form of mounds about 5 metres across, and are situated at the foot of a well-wooded range of hills, in the midst of a wild and formidable scrub. There is no local tradition concerning the factory, since the present population moved into the district comparatively recently, but the likelihood is that it was established in the mid-15th century, that is during the reign of king Tiloka of Chiengmai (r. 1442-1487), and in the wake of the wars between Chiengmai and Ayuthya during which Sri Satchanalai and Sukhothai were repeatedly overrun by one side or the other. Spinks presents evidence suggesting that stoppage at the Sawankoloke factory was sudden and traumatic.

Yet it does not appear that Sankampaeng inherited the full technical and artistic expertise of Sawankoloke. Indeed at first glance there would appear to be little or nothing to connect the two, other than the fact that underglaze iron-black is the standard form of decoration at Sankampaeng as of course it is of one important family of Sawankoloke wares, and that the double-fish design, the commonest and most characteristic motive employed, could perhaps be said to be derived from the single fish motive as found at Sukhothai (no. 162, etc.) and Sawankoloke (no. 217), reduced though it is at Sankampaeng to the condition of a graphic cliché.

One is impressed by the paucity of vessel-types, as well as by the number of pieces bent and warped in firing, and may well doubt whether such a thing as a perfect piece of Sankampaeng decorated ware now exists. Admittedly the only examples we know come from the kiln-site itself, where they are dug up during the rainy season by the assiduous peasantry (and afterwards bought up by the no less assiduous Japanese). This circumstance serves to introduce another, well worth remarking. It is that Sankampaeng decorated ware did not go for export, as did the decorated wares of Sukhothai and Sawankoloke. Neither the Locsins nor Orsay de Flines so much as illustrate a single piece, nor does Spinks. Nor has the present author ever seen one. Included in the present exhibition is a plain tall black jar, no. 350, here identified as from Sankampaeng, which was indeed found in Indonesia, and Spinks illustrates another also found in Indonesia, and Fox one from Calatagan in the Philippines. But to all intents and purposes the ceramic trade to the Archipelago, as far as Thailand was concerned, ended in the 15th century when south China was just getting into its stride. The Sankampaeng kiln, according to Nimmanahaeminda, stopped production soon after 1558 when the Burmese captured the northern Thai kingdom and, he says, took away the artists, artisans, and craftsmen to Burma.

Perhaps I should add that excellent reproductions of Sankampaeng decorated wares are to-day being made at the celadon factories round Chiengmai. You are also cautioned to beware of a line of brown-glazed kendis, emanating from Chiengmai, skillfully modelled in animal forms, and cleverly antiqued. They may be detected by their somewhat lurid yellow ochre biscuit.

*   *   *

The kilns at Kalong were discovered in 1933 by Praya Nakon Prah Ram at a site near the recently settled Tungman village in Vieng Papao district of Chiengrai province, 100 kms north-east of Sankampaeng. The two factories are thought to be contemporary, but at Kalong the technical standard is far higher and the decorative designs more varied, bolder, more artistically conceived and deployed, and quite lacking the spartan and almost impoverished look of Sankampaeng decorated ware.

It has been suggested, and the present writer agrees, that the presence of Tzŭ Chou is discernable in these boldly contrasted designs. The question is whether this was due to a renaissance consciously based on Sukhothai, and perhaps occasioned by Sukhothai potters being brought north after the military campaigns, or whether to a fresh influx of patterns from Tzŭ Chou itself, or, yet a third possibility, whether it was an original development on the part of the Kalong potters working on the bare memory of the Sukhothai pattern-book.

Sankampaeng and Kalong share certain vessel-shapes, and the likelihood is the two factories were familiar with each other's products. The technical characteristics of the wares are described in the notes which follow.

*   *   *

I would like if I may to add a few unconnected afterthoughts by way of a postscript to what has been written above, on a subject about which we admittedly have much to learn. It might, for instance, be worth considering whether the *whole* of the Sukhothai *oeuvre* is not an offshoot of the Annamese underglaze iron-black tradition. Then the Tzŭ Chou influence upon Sukhothai, if really present, would have come *via* Annam rather than directly from China through an incursus of Tzŭ Chou potters, as is generally conceived. Again, I wrote earlier that Sukhothai slipwares were liable to degradation of their glaze, sometimes to the point where it totally disappears. It occurs to me that in some examples glaze may never have been applied at all.

Secondly, though I have consistently described the dark underglaze pigment on Annamese, Sukhothai and Sawankoloke painted wares as iron (i.e. ferric oxide), it occurs to me that this need not necessarily always have been the case, and that manganese may sometimes have been used. This might account for the distinct purple tinge seen on so many of the Sukhothai on-slip painted bowls and dishes.

Next, it is perhaps worth mentioning that the attribution of the Sawankoloke brown-glazed monochromes to the Chalieng site and the pre-Sukhothai period, commonly made, seems to rely on an original observation of Praya Nakon Prah Ram's, who in 1936 stated that he had come across numbers of such sherds embedded in the east bank of the Yom River opposite the Temple of the Great Relic, which is thought to stand on the site of ancient Chalieng. This does not mean of course that a factory ever existed there, nor do I think such a suggestion has ever been made. But neither does it mean that the sherds are contemporary with Khmer Chalieng. Sherds are to be found everywhere along the banks of the Yom River, and their relative depth in such a context is no reliable evidence as to their relative antiquity, as Praya Nakon Prah Ram supposed. Moreover Mr. Dale Keller of Hong Kong has in his possession a brown-glazed Sawankoloke waster fused with a Sawankoloke celadon waster, which can only mean that they were fired together, at the same time and in the same kiln. Add to this the demonstrable stylistic connection between the brown-glazed monochromes and the other Sawankoloke lines, and the absence of any such connection between them and the Khmer oeuvre, and we can safely eliminate the hypothesised Chalieng period and product from the history of Thai ceramics.

Lastly may I draw attention to the Chinese blue-and-white bowl illustrated on p. 194, which was in fact bought in Bangkok. It has a scribbled Chinese character on the inside centre medallion, similar to that of no. 67, which is Annamese. The Chinese bowl might thus date from the 15th century, though in form it closely resembles small export bowls of the Wan-li period. The interesting thing is that its décor, comprising 6 contiguous oblong panels containing alternating cross-hatching and vegetal scrolls, is precisely that which occurs over and over again on Sawankoloke under-glaze iron-black covered boxes and potiches, being indeed the standard motive among these wares. It is difficult to believe that the Chinese could have borrowed the motive from the Thai, being very adequately stocked with decorative motives of their own. More probably it was of Chinese origin, was next assimilated into Annamese blue-and-white (e.g. nos 52, 53, 71), and thence found its way to Sawankoloke in the first half of the 15th century.

BIBLIOGRAPHY

Here follows a list of books refered to in the Introduction and Descriptive Notes, by means of which comparisons may be made between ceramics illustrated in this catalogue and those in other collections:

d'Argencé, i.e. R.-Y. Lefebvre d'Argencé, *Les céramiques à base chocolatée au Musée Louis-Finot de l'École Française d'Extrême-Orient à Hanoi,* Paris 1958

Bangkok, i.e. Bangkok National Museum, *Exhibition of Masterpieces from Private Collections, 6th March - 6th April 1968,* Bangkok 1968

Diskul I, i.e. M.C. Subhadradis Diskul, *Guide to the Old Town of Sukhothai,* Bangkok n.d., (pamphlet, 12 pp)

Diskul II, i.e. M.C. Subhadradis Diskul, *Guide to the Town of Sri Satchanalai,* Bangkok n.d., (pamphlet, 12 pp)

Dublin, i.e. Municipal Gallery of Modern Art, Dublin, *Chinese Ceramics 10th-17th Century* (Arts Council exhibition), Dublin 1967

Flines, i.e. E. W. Van Orsoy de Flines, *Gids voor de Keramische Verzameling (Uitheemse Keramiek),* Batavia (Djakarta) 1949. Translated as *Guide to the Ceramic Collection (Foreign Ceramics),* Djakarta 1969

Fox, i.e. R.B. Fox, "The Calatagan excavations. Two fifteenth century burial sites in Batangas", in *Philippine Studies* vol. 7, no. 3 (August 1959), pp.

Freer, i.e. The Freer Gallery of Art, *Ming Porcelains in the Freer Gallery of Art,* Washington (Smithsonian Institution) 1953

Goloubew, i.e. V. Goloubew, "La province de Thanh-hoa et sa céramique", in *Revue des Arts Asiatiques* tom. vii, no. 2 (Paris 1931), pp. 112-116

Griswold, i.e. A.B. Griswold, *Towards a History of Sukhodaya Art,* Bangkok (The Fine Arts Department) 1967

Groslier, i.e. G. Groslier, *Recherches sur les Cambodgiens d'après les textes et les monuments depuis les premiers siècles de notre ère,* Paris 1921, pp. 129-133 (La Céramique)

Hobson, i.e. R. L. Hobson, "Chinese porcelain at Constantinople", in *Transactions of the Oriental Ceramic Society* (1933-4), pp. 9-14

Indiana, i.e. Indiana University, *The Arts of Thailand. A Handbook of the Architecture, Sculpture and Painting of Thailand (Siam).* By A.B. Griswold and others, Bloomington 1960

Jenyns, i.e. Soame Jenyns, *Ming Pottery and Porcelain,* London 1953

Locsin, i.e. Leandro and Cecilia Locsin, *Oriental Ceramics Discovered in the Philippines*, Rutland (Vermont) and Tokyo 1967

Nimmana., i.e. Kraisri Nimmanahaeminda, *Sankampaeng Glazed Pottery*, Chiengmai 1960

Okuda, i.e. Okuda Seiichi, *Annam Toji Zukan [or] Annamese Ceramics*, Tokyo 1954

Penkala, i.e. Maria Penkala, *Far Eastern Ceramics*, The Hague 1963

Philadelphia, i.e. Philadelphia Museum, "An exhibition of blue-decorated porcelain of the Ming dynasty", being *Philadelphia Museum Bulletin* vol. xliv, no. 233 (Autumn 1949)

Pope I, i.e. J.A. Pope, *Fourteenth-Century Blue-and-White. A Group of Chinese Porcelains in the Topkapu Sarayi Muzesi, Istanbul*, Washington (Smithsonian Institution) 1952

Pope II, i.e. J.A. Pope, *Chinese Porcelains from the Ardebil Shrine*, Washington (Smithsonian Institution) 1956

Ram, i.e. Praya Nakon Prah Ram, "Tai pottery", in *The Journal of the Siam Society* vol. xxix, pt 1 (August 1936), pp. 13-36

Silice, i.e. A. Silice and G. Groslier, "La céramique dans l'ancien Cambodge (essai d'inventaire général)", in *Arts et Archéologie Khmers* tom. 2, 1924-1926, Paris ?1926, pp. 27-63

Spinks I, i.e. C.N. Spinks, *Siamese Pottery in Indonesia*, Bangkok (The Siam Society) 1959

Spinks II, i.e. C.N. Spinks, *The Ceramic Wares of Siam*, Bangkok (The Siam Society) 1965

Stockholm, i.e. Ostasiatiska Museet, *Ming Blue-and-White* from Swedish Collections, Museum of Far Eastern Art Exhibition Catalogue No. 1, Stockholm 1964

Note. In identifying floral decorative motives recourse has been had to the two illustrated catalogues by Pope listed above, as well as to d'Argencé and one or two other scholars who have attempted botanical identifications. The present writer does not necessarily accept all these identifications as correct, but that is of minor importance. What is important is that everybody should be enabled to know what is being talked about, by reference to a standard text. In the same way with the non-naturalistic motives I have tried to adopt the nomenclature habitually used by ceramic historians, though some of the terms used to describe parts of the body of the pot, particularly the foot, are not in universal use and are to some extent idiosyncratic. I am grateful to Dr. Chang Kiaw Lan for making a few independant botanical identifications.

137

DESCRIPTIVE NOTES

GROUP ONE: KHMER WARES

1 Jar

Having the beak, eyes, and tail of an owl, skillfully modelled; the body divided into 6 vertical panels by groups of 4 or 5 incised lines, converging below; covered in a dark matt *temmoku*-type glaze with a grey biscuit; the foot plain, button-shaped, and with a flat base,

Ht (of mouth) 6.9 cm.

Mrs. Helen Ling

12th century, Angkor Wat type, bought in Bangkok. Together with nos 2 and 5 this jar has the 'well' interior which Mr. Frasché believes indicates manufacture at a kiln inside Thailand.

2 Covered jar

In the form of a pangolin or anteater (*Manis*) and with a top-shaped conical lid; with the animal's head and tail modelled in the round, its strongly re-curved back with two systems of parallel diagonal incised lines, with indications of scales in the lumbar region and at the base of the tail, and with its paws modelled in relief upon the uncarved base; covered in a brown *temmoku*-type glaze, partly abraded and revealing a pale purple body beneath; the foot with a buff biscuit,

Ht (with lid) 8.2 cm., l. 9.7 cm.

Mrs. Helen Ling

3 Jar

Of flattened globular form; with a dark matt *temmoku*-type glaze on a brown biscuit; the mouthrim raised; the body neatly partitioned into 7 panels by 7 groups of 3 parallel vertical incised lines; the lower shoulder neatly scored with horizontal circular single bands, the upper shoulder with a relief band chiselled into small regular rhombs; the neck with 4 fine horizontal circular scored bands; the lower body and foot unglazed, and with a dark ochre biscuit; the foot with a flat base having a slightly raised perimeter,

Ht 8.2 cm.; d. 14.9 cm.

Mrs. Helen Ling

12th century, Angkor Wat type. For an illustration of the foot see p. 190, upper left.

4 Jar

Of flattened globular form; with a dark matt *temmoku*-type glaze; the mouthrim raised, and with a collar of carved circular decorative bands; the shoulder with an incised scalloped border between two pairs of carved decorative bands; the body partitioned into 13 panels by 13 pairs of vertical carved striations, closed below by a moulded circular band; the lower body and moulded foot unglazed, and with a yellowish-brown biscuit; the perimeter of the foot slightly raised, as with no. 3,

D. 13.5 cm.

The Sinclair Collection

12th century, Angkor Wat type, from Indonesia.

5 Miniature covered jar

Of a flattened globular form, and with a flat conical top-shaped lid; the lid and upper shoulder with several incised circular decorative bands, closely spaced like grooves on a gramophone record, those on the lid with some radial lines crossing them; the lid and upper body covered in a dark brown *temmoku*-type glaze; the foot moderately tall, splayed outwards above, and inwards below down to a plain, slightly concave base having a roughly-incised circular score upon it; the foot with a grey biscuit,

Ht (with lid) 6.2 cm.

Mr. Gilbert Zeullig

6 Bottle

Of depressed globular form, and with a nozzle-like mouth; the neck with 2 incised circular decorative bands; the body with 3 groups of 4, 4, and 5 diagonally incised striations; covered in a dark *temmoku*-type glaze; the lower body and plain foot unglazed, and with a charcoal biscuit; the base with a slightly raised perimeter,

Ht 6.7 cm.

Mrs. Helen Ling

7   Jar

Somewhat in the shape of a Laotian bronze drum; the body bi-carinate, the shoulder almost flat; covered with a dark matt *temmoku*-type glaze; the shoulder with four circular bands of chiselled ornament similar in general character to that of nos. 3 and 4; the lower body and foot unglazed; the foot plain and the base slightly concave, with a grey biscuit,

Ht 7.6 cm., d. 9.2 cm.

Mrs. Helen Ling

12th century, Angkor Wat type. Known to have come from Cambodia.

8   Incense burner

In the form of a flattened globular jar upon a cup-stand; the jar with two moulded circular decorative bands on the neck, and two incised scalloped bands on the shoulder; all covered with a mottled dark-brown *temmoku*-type glaze, much abraded at the turning-points; the foot flat and crudely thrown, and the body with a light-grey, granular, and much pitted biscuit, Ht 9.8 cm.

The University of Singapore

12th-13th century, Bayon type. Acquired at Siem-réap and stated to have been found in the north moat at Angkor Thom. It must therefore post-date, if only by a few years, the digging of the moat about 1190 A.D.

9   Brush pot

Of pomegranate form with a small mouth on a raised crater-like neck; the body divided into 10 panels by means of groups of 3 or 4 incised vertical lines; all covered with a dark-brown *temmoku*-type glaze that has run in tear-drops; the lower body and foot unglazed, and with a dark red-brown biscuit; the foot uncarved, the base slightly concave,

Ht 8.2 cm.

The University of Singapore
From Indonesia.

10   Bowl

Of crucible shape; with a worn dark chocolate-brown glaze; the plain foot crudely thrown, the base concave, and with a grey biscuit,

D. 9.2 cm.

Mr. William Willetts
From Indonesia.

11   Bottle

Carinate, and with a high, nearly straight-sided shoulder, short neck, and mouth with an everted lip; covered in a dark-brown matt *temmoku*-type glaze with greenish tints; the uncarved foot unglazed, and with a dark-grey biscuit; the base somewhat concave,

Ht 16.5 cm.

The University of Singapore
Given by the Government of Cambodia.

12   Urn

Carinate, with a high straight-sided shoulder, the body sloping steeply in towards the broken foot, which was probably on a short stem; the upper shoulder strongly ribbed by means of four carved and undercut decorative bands between which is a single band of cord-pattern; the lower shoulder similarly ribbed, and with a corded band; the body unglazed, with a dark-red biscuit, and a calcareous splash on the shoulder,

Present ht 27.3 cm.

The University of Malaya

11th century, Baphuon type. Given by the Government of Cambodia, and stated to have come from the West Baray at Angkor. A closely similar vessel, with moulded foot complete, appears in *Silice*, pl. 11, no. 4, from Tréang, Takeo.

13   Bottle

Of depressed globular shape with a wide and slightly flaring neck, the mouthrim broken; the upper shoulder with a tight combed zig-zag pattern between 2 pairs of carved circular decorative bands; all covered with a thin, pale-green glaze of celadon type; there is no foot, the glaze flowing patchily over the whole lower body, which discloses a beige-coloured biscuit,

Present ht 19 cm.

The University of Malaya

10th century, Kulen type. Given by the Government of Cambodia, and stated to have come from the cemetery area north of Srah Srang, Angkor. A similar bottle from near Trak, Battembang province is shown in *Silice*, fig. 24, no. 5.

14   Bottle

Of a tall ovoid shape, and with narrow columnar neck, the mouth broken; with two circular wavy bands scored on the shoulder between two circular incised horizontal bands; covered in a warm brown ferruginous glaze, with green tints, and an eroded lighter patch with an orange-skin texture on the shoulder; the foot plain; the base slightly concave, and with a dark-red biscuit,

Ht 26 cm.

The University of Singapore

Given by the Government of Cambodia and stated to have come from the Angkor region.

15   Jar

Of exotic shape, with a domed shoulder, short neck and flared mouth, and two vertical ring-handles where the domed shoulder joins the body; covered with a ferruginous dark-brown glaze speckled with yellowish-white, and resembling Chinese 18th-century "tea-dust"; the foot roughly turned, and with a deep circular incision near its edge; the base of a reddish-brown colour, the paste brick-red; the lower body, evidently reduced, exhibiting a grey biscuit,

Ht 17.6 cm.

The Sinclair Collection

From the Celebes.

16   Bottle

Of *yü hu ch'un p'ing* shape, the neck rather short; covered in a speckled dark-brown ferruginous glaze similar to that of no. 15; the lower body unglazed, and with a pinkish-grey biscuit; the flat foot button-shaped, similar to that of no. 1, and bearing the mark of a coarse cutting-cord like a magnified thumb-print,

Ht 9.8 cm.

The Sinclair Collection

From the Celebes. For an illustration of the foot see p. 109, upper right. A similar print is seen in *Locsin*, p. 221, pl. 17, a brown-glazed jarlet from Santa Ana.

17   Jar

With constricted neck and flared mouthrim, and with two horizontal ring-handles on the shoulder; covered in an irregular and patchy dark olive-green celadon glaze, except on parts of the lower body which exhibit a pinkish-grey biscuit; the flat unglazed foot closely similar to that of no. 16, and with an almost identical 'thumb-print',

Ht 15.9 cm.

The Sinclair Collection

From the Celebes.

18   Jar

Shaped like a small ostrich-egg, and of about the same colour, lifted slightly on a tall flared foot which was perhaps thrown separately; the neck having a flat collar or 'ruff', cross-hatched with incised lines; covered in a thin ferruginous pale olive-green glaze, of irregular application, similar to that of nos 13 and 17; the button-like foot flat, and bearing the 'thumb-print' seen in nos 16 and 17,

Ht 9.2 cm.

The Sinclair Collection

10th century, Kulen type. Bought at Phnom Penh.

19   Jar

Globular, with a short tubular neck and rounded mouthrim; the shoulder with two circular registers of oblique gouged

(cont.)

striations, the body with a third register of similar more-or-less vertical striations; covered with an irregular mottled ferruginous glaze, olive-green in parts, dark-brown in others; the flat base roughly turned, and almost covered in glaze, and somewhat similar to that of no. 13,

Ht 11.1 cm.

The Sinclair Collection

Purchased at Phnom Penh; for a similar jar see *Silice*, pl. 12, no. 5 from Tréang Takeo.

20 Water dropper

In the form of a Mandarin duck with open back (not however communicating with the interior of the vessel), and with moulded anatomical parts; covered in a crackled and variegated dark olive-green glaze markedly similar to that of no. 17; the flat base showing a rough charcoal-coloured biscuit,

Ht 8.4 cm.

The Sinclair Collection

From the Celebes.

GROUP TWO: ANNAMESE WARES

Family 1. Wares decorated in underglaze blue.

21 Dish

The rim unglazed, the flat lip with a classic scroll; the cavetto with 6 stylised lotuses in a scroll; the centre medallion with an elaborate peony wreath surrounded by a scalloped-petal border; the outside wall with 16 lotus panels enclosing leaf-forms; the boundary circles drawn in a pale underglaze blue, the rest in a brighter mauvish-blue; the carved foot unglazed, but the base coated with a thin opaque brownish-white glaze,

D. 37.5 cm.

The University of Singapore

This dish, and nos. 22 and 26, may be roughly dated to the mid-15th century on the basis of a bottle in the Topkapu

Sarayi Muzesi bearing a date corresponding to the year 1450. Cf. *Hobson*, p. 13 and pl. 4.

22 Dish

The rim unglazed, the flat lip with a classic scroll; the cavetto with 6 stylised lotuses in a scroll; the centre medallion with a full-blown peony wreath, its border empty; the outside wall with 14 lotus panels enclosing leaf-forms; all painted in an intense underglaze Royal blue; the carved foot unglazed, and with a 'chocolate base',

D. 35.2 cm.

The University of Singapore

23 Dish

With unglazed rim, the flat lip with a classic scroll; the cavetto with 3 groups of three plantain leaves; the centre medallion with a brisky-drawn stand of bamboo; the outside wall with 11 lotus panels enclosing leaf-forms; all painted in an intense underglaze blue-black; the carved footrim unglazed, but the base with a patchy opaque oatmeal-coloured glaze,

D. 35.6 cm.

The University of Singapore

24 Dish

The rim unglazed, the flat lip with a classic scroll; the cavetto with 3 lotus sprays alternating with 3 of peonies; the centre medallion representing a lotus pond (in which may be seen a fresh-water prawn or shrimp), surrounded by a border of 6 cloud-scrolls, each in a separate panel; the outside wall with 12 lotus panels enclosing leaf-forms; all painted in a silvery underglaze blue-grey; the unglazed footrim with a putty-coloured biscuit, and the base covered with a gum-coloured glaze,

D. 35.5 cm.

The Sinclair Collection

Representations of lotus ponds occur on, for example, *Pope II*, pls. 7 and 8 (Ardebil 29.38, 29.40, and 29.41), but the closest parallel is upon the *mei-p'ing* vase illustrated in *Pope I*, pl. 27 (T.K.S. 1398); see also *Pope I*, pls. 4 and 5 (T.K.S. 1428).

25 Dish

The rim unglazed, the flat lip with a classic scroll; the cavetto with 6 peonies in a scroll; the centre medallion with a peony wreath surrounded by a lotus-petal border; the outside wall with 11 lotus panels enclosing leaf-forms; all in a deep indigo underglaze blue; the carved foot-rim unglazed, and the base with a spirally brushed and scraped toffee-coloured slip,

D. 35.2 cm.

The University of Singapore

An illustration of the outside of this dish appears on p. 190, lower left.

26 Dish

The rim unglazed, the flat lip with a classic scroll; the cavetto with 6 peonies in a scroll; and the centre medallion with a peony spray inside a scalloped-petal border; the outside wall with 16 lotus panels enclosing leaf-forms; all painted in a strong underglaze Prussian blue with much line-work; the carved foot unglazed, and the base with a brushed-on light-brown slip,

D. 35.5 cm.

The University of Singapore

27 Dish

With unglazed rim, the flat lip with a classic scroll; the cavetto with 6 six-petalled rosettes in a scroll; the centre medallion with a *shih tzŭ* feline playing with a brocaded ball and contained within a scalloped-petal border; the outside wall with 14 lotus panels enclosing leaf-forms; the unglazed footrim with a putty-coloured biscuit, the base with a scraped-off light-brown slip,

D. 36.5 cm.

The Sinclair Collection

28 Dish

With unglazed rim, the flat lip with a classic scroll; the whole interior occupied with a large 6-pointed "Sassanian asterisk" enclosing a chrysanthemum rosette, and with leaf-sprays between the points; the outside wall with 12 lotus panels enclosing leaf-forms; all painted in a deep under-glaze blue-black; the carved foot unglazed, and with a spirally scraped 'chocolate base',

D. 36.2 cm.

The University of Singapore

For a similar dish see *Okuda*, figs. 72-3. An illustration of the outside of the dish appears on p. 190, lower right.

29 Dish

With unglazed rim, the flat lip with a classic scroll; the cavetto with 6 peonies in a scroll; the centre medallion with a lotus wreath surrounded by a border of interrupted classic scroll; the outside wall with 12 lotus panels enclosing leaf-forms; all painted in underglaze blue-black; the carved footrim and base covered in an opaque straw-coloured glaze; some old cracks,

D. 36.5 cm.

Mr. William Willetts

I call the 4-petalled rosettes of the cavetto 'peonies' in conformity with *d'Argence'*, tab. II. 4, labelled 'pivoines'.

30 Dish

With unglazed rim; the flat lip marked by a plain underglaze-blue band; the cavetto with a scroll containing 6 lotus blooms; the centre medallion with a lotus wreath within a scalloped-petal border; the outside wall with 11 lotus panels enclosing leaf-forms; all painted in a faded underglaze blue-black; the carved footrim unglazed, but the base with a brownish-white partly scraped-off glaze,

D. 35.8 cm.

The University of Singapore

31 Dish

With a foliate unglazed rim, the flat lip painted in underglaze-blue foliations following the contour of the rim; the cavetto with 6 chrysanthemums in a scroll;

the centre medallion with a *shih-tzŭ* feline pursuing a brocaded ball and surrounded by a scalloped-petal border; the outside wall decorated as the cavetto; the carved foot unglazed, but the base partly covered with a spirally-scraped straw-coloured glaze,

D. 34.7 cm.

The University of Singapore

Cf. no. 27.

32 Dish

With unglazed rim, the flat lip undecorated; the cavetto with a scroll of 6 six-petalled rosettes; the centre medallion with a peony wreath enclosed in a scalloped-petal border; the outside wall with 13 lotus panels enclosing leaf-forms; all painted in a solid underglaze blue-black; the unglazed footrim with a beige-coloured biscuit, the foot with a 'chocolate base',

D. 35.5 cm.

The Sinclair Collection

For a similar dish see *Okuda*, fig. 70; cf. also nos. 21 and 22.

33 Dish

With unglazed rim, the flat lip with a classic scroll; the cavetto with a scroll of 6 peonies; the centre medallion with a lotus wreath surrounded by a border containing cloud-scrolls; the outside wall with 11 lotus panels enclosing leaf-forms; all painted in a pale blackish underglaze-blue; the carved foot unglazed, and with a 'chocolate base',

D. 36.2 cm.

The University of Singapore

34 Dish

The rim unglazed; the lip with a classic scroll, the cavetto with a scroll of 6 peonies; the centre medallion with a sea-perch set amid waterweeds (including eel-grass, lotus, water-chesnut, duck-weed, and feathery grasses), all surrounded by a border of cloud-scrolls; the outside wall with 10 lotus panels enclosing leaf-forms; all painted in a solid underglaze blue-

black; the unglazed footrim with a putty-coloured biscuit, the foot with a 'chocolate base',

D. 36.2 cm.

The Sinclair Collection

The derivation from such 14th-century Chinese prototypes as seen in *Pope II*, pl. 9 (Ardebil 29.42) is obvious. For related Annamese examples see *Okuda*, figs. 68, 69, and *Flines*, pl. 39, (Djakarta).

35 Vase

Of *mei-p'ing* form and with a wide mouth; painted in a pallid grey-blue pigment under a semi-opaque milky glaze; the upper shoulder with 4 round-ended long panels containing vegetal forms, alternating with diapers; the lower shoulder with four interrupted classic scrolls; the body with a peony scroll, and the lower body with a band of pendent leaf- and flame-forms; the cover with knop-handle and a lotus-leaf rosette,

Ht (with cover) 26.2 cm.

Professor and Mrs. K. J. Ratnam

36 Covered box

Of flattened globular form; the body decorated in underglaze blue with a classic scroll below the mouthrim, a continuous cloud-collar scroll on the shoulder, alternating lotus and peony blossoms on the body, and a lotus-petal band, below which is another of 8 diapers, on the lower body; the cover with vegetal forms around the plain knop-handle; the footrim carved and with a white biscuit,

Ht (with cover). 7.6 cm.

Mr and Mrs Trevor Rutter

Perhaps early 15th century. For a bowl of similar shape *(po kang)* and with a similarly-disposed décor see *Philadelphia*, no. 59 (Leventritt), of the Hsüan-tê period.

37 Dish

With unglazed rim and a flat lip; painted in underglaze blue-black; the centre medallion with three fish sharing a single head in eelgrass and enclosed in a border comprising 4 cloud-scrolls; the cavetto with a lotus scroll of 4 blooms; the outside wall with 6 lotus panels containing leaf-forms; the footrim carved, the foot with a 'chocolate base',

D. 23.2 cm.

Mr. K. T. Goh

38 Dish

With unglazed rim, the flattened lip painted with a classic scroll in underglaze blue-black; the centre medallion with a chrysanthemum wreath enclosed in a scalloped-petal border; the outside wall with 12 lotus panels enclosing leaf-forms; the footrim carved, and with a putty-coloured biscuit; the foot with a spirally coated 'chocolate base'; some fire-cracks,

D. 24.6 cm.

The University of Singapore

39 Dish

With unglazed rim and flattened lip; painted in underglaze blue-black, the cavetto with a scroll of 4 lotus blooms; the centre medallion with a stand of bamboo enclosed within a border of 4 cloud-scrolls; the outside wall with 8 lotus panels enclosing leaf-forms; the carved footrim unglazed and with a putty-coloured biscuit; the foot with a spirally-applied 'chocolate base',

D. 23.6 cm.

The University of Singapore

40 Covered box

Of a tall cup-shape and with a flared foot; the body decorated in bright underglaze blue with two carefully-drawn horizontal bands of cloud-collar points above and below, connected across by vertical lines; the sides of the lid with a band of lotus panels enclosing leaf-forms; the moulded flat top with a chrysanthemum spray framed by a beaded border; the outer side of the footrim with a chocolate slip; the under side unglazed, and with a putty-coloured biscuit; the base glazed,

Ht 8.7 cm.

Mr. K. T. Goh

41 Jar

With a long S-shaped profile and broad mouth and foot; decorated in underglaze blue on a cream biscuit, the shoulder with a border of 5 cloud-collar points enclosing trefoils, the body with three magpies in flight between grasses, the lower body with a belt of lotus-panels enclosing leaf-forms; the under side of the footrim wide, and showing a cream biscuit; the base with a spirally-scraped chocolate slip,

Ht 17.4 cm.

Mr. K. T. Goh

For a similar shape and décor see *d'Argencé* pl. 11, nos. 1a-d.

42 Pug dog

In a sitting posture; the animal's features and fur delineated in underglaze blue; the body covered in a translucent colourless glaze, the flat foot unglazed, and with a putty-coloured biscuit,

Ht 11.7 cm.

Mr. K. T. Goh

43 Mandarin duck water dropper

The body strongly moulded, and the features picked out in underglaze blue; all covered in a milky-white glaze on an off-white biscuit,

Ht 7.1 cm.

Mr. K. T. Goh

44 Covered box

Moulded into 6 lobes and decorated in underglaze blue with 6 two-point foliate medallion panels containing alternating peony and peach sprays; the cover with a flat top featuring a scrolled design reserved on a blue ground, and with two floral forms surrounding the plain knop-handle, of 'lotus bud' shape; the lower body with a border of lotus petals; covered with a translucent glaze inside and outside; the foot carved and unglazed, and with a cream-coloured biscuit,

Ht (with lid) 9.1 cm.

Mr. S. R. Parker

On the basis of the Ming Chinese blue-and-white design repertory, the box may perhaps be assigned to the late 16th century.

45 Covered box

On a raised foot; the lid and body decorated with 6 incised panels containing alternating leaf-sprays and concentric rhomboids; the lid top with a scallop-edged underglaze-blue medallion featuring a scrolled pattern and central rosette; lid, body, and base covered with a translucent glaze; the carved footrim showing a white biscuit,

D. 8 cm.

Mr. and Mrs. E. M. T. Lu

46 Covered box

Body and lid divided by means of 6 sets of 3 gouged vertical lines into 6 vertical panels containing alternating incised leaf-sprays and concentric rhomboids; the flat lid with a medallion featuring a peony spray; all covered in a translucent glaze; the carved footrim unglazed, and with a cream-coloured biscuit; the base with a thin opaque white glaze,

D. 8.2 cm.

The University of Singapore

Cf. nos. 44 & 45, with which 46 is presumably contemporary.

47 Covered box

The body with an incised floral scroll; the lower body with lotus-petal border in underglaze blue; the sides of the lid incised with 10 panels containing alternating leaf-forms and diapers; the cream-biscuited flat top-surface of the lid moulded, butterpat-wise, to represent a phoenix; the inside glazed, and the foot carved, and with a yellowish-cream biscuit,

D. 10.3 cm.

Mr. K. T. Goh

48 Vase

Of a squat *mei-p'ing* shape, the sides moulded into 8 panels; below the mouthrim a key-fret border in underglaze blue; the upper shoulder with a band of cloud-collar points containing leaf-forms; the body with 4 delicately-drawn ogival medallions, each formed by two confronted cloud-collar points and each enclosing a peony scroll, and with confronted medallion tips between; the lower body with a horizontal band of cloud-scroll above, and below an upright band of tall lotus-panels containing leaf-forms; the carved foot largely unglazed, and with a light-grey biscuit,

Ht 16.8 cm.

Mr. K. T. Goh

For similar medallions on a Chinese gourd-shaped bottle of the 14th century cf. *Pope I*, pl. 34 (T.K.S. 1473)

49 Bowl

With slightly everted mouth; decorated in underglaze blue-black, the inside lip with a classic scroll, the centre medallion with a peony spray, the outside wall with a band of 4 peonies alternating with leaf-sprays above, and a band of lotus-panels enclosing leaf-forms below; the high foot carved, the under and inner sides of the footrim showing a cream slip, the foot with a 'chocolate base',

D. 16.5 cm.

The University of Singapore

For the 14th-century Chinese prototype cf. *Pope I*, pl. 24 (T.K.S. 1376). Cf. also *Flines*, pl. 93, left and right (Djakarta), from the south Celebes. The two last are Annamese.

50 Bowl

With slightly everted lip; decorated in underglaze blue-black, the outside wall with a scroll of 4 lotus blooms above and a lotus-petal border below; the centre medallion with the character *fu*, 福 , 'happiness'; the carved foot with a cream-coloured biscuit,

D. 9 cm.

Mr. and Mrs. Frank Lammers

Cf. *d'Argencé*, pl. 6b, showing the interior of a bowl with an almost identically brushed *fu* character, bought in 1925 at Cong-vi in Hai-duong province.

51 Bowl

With scalloped mouthrim slightly everted; decorated in underglaze blue, the outside wall with a band of 4 peonies alternating with leaf-sprays above, and 4 cloud-scrolls below; the inside of the lip with 8 scalloped petals, the centre medallion with a floral spray; the carved footrim with an off-white biscuit, and the foot with a 'chocolate base',

D. 8.7 cm.

Mr. and Mrs. Frank Lammers

52 Jarlet

Moulded into 12 lobes and painted in underglaze-blue; the body with 3 panels containing leaf-sprays, alternating with 3 filled with diapers enclosing crosses; the shoulder similarly decorated; the foot, with carefully carved footrim and shallow base, showing a beige-coloured biscuit,

Ht 3.3 cm.

Dr. and Mrs. K. H. Lim

Similar in form to nos. 121 and 128. For an illustration of the foot see p. 191, upper left.

53 Covered box

With underglaze-blue decoration disposed in eight panels on the body and the sides of the lid, and containing alternating leaf-sprays and diapers (on the lid) or diagonally-crossed bands (on the body); the flat top edged with a similar border surrounding a phoenix with wings outstretched among cloud-scrolls; the box and lid glazed within; the foot carved, and with a chalky-white biscuit,

D. 10.4 cm.

Mr. Stensan Y. H. Wong

The phoenix would seem to be related to those on the David vases dated 1351.

54 Jarlet

Of amphora form, with three ring-handles on the shoulder; decorated in underglaze blue, the lip with tiny figured forms, the shoulder with a collar of lotus leaves, the body with a scroll of 6 six-petalled

rosettes; and the lower body with a band of lotus panels enclosing leaf-forms; the glaze bluish, and with a white-veined crackle; the foot uncarved and flat, and with a beige biscuit,

Ht 9 cm.

Dr. and Mrs. K. H. Lim

55 Jar

Of globular form, with four ring-handles on the shoulder; delicately painted in underglaze blue, with 4 scalloped petals on the shoulder and 4 peonies on the body; the carved foot with a putty-coloured biscuit,

Ht 7.9 cm.

The University of Singapore

56 Jar

Of globular form; painted in pale underglaze blue-black with a circle of lotus leaves on the shoulder and a scroll of 4 lotus blooms on the body; with 3 summary spirals on the lower body; the carved footrim with a beige biscuit, and the foot with a 'chocolate base',

Ht 9.5 cm.

The University of Singapore

57 Jar

Of globular form, moulded into 8 flat panels; with underglaze-blue decoration comprising 4 scalloped petals on the shoulder, and on the body 4 octagonal panels, each containing an epidendron-like plant, with intervening smaller panels of crossed diagonals; the rather deeply carved foot with an off-white biscuit,

Ht 7.2 cm.

Mr. and Mrs. Frank Lammers

58 Jar

Of octagonal form and with a flat shoulder; the decoration, in underglaze blue, comprising a lotus-leaf collar, and on the body 4 main panels each containing an orchid-like plant alternating with smaller panels filled with wave pattern; the lower body with 4 cloud-scrolls; the carved footrim and base un-glazed and with a putty-coloured biscuit,

Ht 8.5 cm.

Mr. William Willetts

59   Jar

Similar to no. 58, but smaller; the 4 main panels on the body each featuring a switch of bamboo; the intervening smaller panels with a diaper pattern; the carved footrim and base unglazed, and with an off-white biscuit,

Ht 7.1 cm.

Mr. William Willetts

60   Bottle

Of *yü hu ch'un-p'ing* shape; decorated in underglaze blue, the inside mouth with 4 vegetal scrolls, the neck with 4 upright plantain leaves, the shoulder with 4 lotus panels, two of which contain brocaded balls and two a downward-pointing feathery leaf-form; the body with 4 oval panels containing upward-pointing fea-thery leaf-forms alternating with columns of wave-pattern, and the lower body with 5 lotus panels enclosing leaf-forms; the carved footrim unglazed and with an oatmeal biscuit, the foot with a very dark 'chocolate base'; the mouth and neck much restored,

Ht 31.6 cm.

The University of Singapore

Perhaps 14th century. Cf. *Philadelphia*, fig. 2 (Boston) for the Chinese prototype; Cf. also *Okuda*, fig. 45, for a closely-similar Annamese example. Of several Annamese examples illustrated in *d'Argencé* one (pl. 8, no. 1a) was bought at Hai-duong, one (pl. 8, no. 2) at Bat-trang, and one (pl. 9, no. 2) was found at Tuyen-quang.

61   Bowl

With everted lip, and standing on a tall footrim; decorated in bright underglaze blue with a 6-petalled blackberry lily blossom within a decorative circular band on the inside bottom; with two similar bands on the upper inside wall; the whole

covered with a somewhat opaque pearly-white glaze; the foot with a 'chocolate base',

D. 11.7 cm.

Mr. K. T. Goh

Perhaps 14th century. For a Chinese example of a similarly centred blackberry lily blossom on a stem-cup cf. *Philadelphia*, fig. 8 (Stevenson). In calling the six-petalled rosette a blackberry-lily *(Belam-canda chinensis)* I am here following *Pope I*, Pl. B, no. 5; it is true this motive could be a stylized lotus, as indeed it appears to be in the case of no. 62.

62   Jarlet

Of globular form; with an underglaze blue decoration of 3 stylized chrysanthe-mum blooms and one lotus; the carved foot with a shallow footrim and putty-coloured biscuit,

Ht 5.7 cm.

Mr. K. T. Goh

Comparison with the now well-known Yüan and early Ming ring-handled blue-and-white jarlets (e.g. *Locsin*, pl. 85) in-dicates a late 14th-century date for no. 62.

63   Covered box

In the form of a crab; the features delineated in underglaze blue, and the carapace similarly decorated with a chrysanthemum spray; much repaired,

L. 11.4 cm.

The Sinclair Collection

The most magnificent of these crab boxes, considerably larger in size and more precisely anatomically sculpted, are in the category of apple-green copper-glazed wares.

64   Pair of miniature fish water droppers

The anatomical parts painted in blue under a transparent glaze on a buff-coloured biscuit,

L. (of each) 5.9 cm.

Mr. Stensan Y. H. Wong

65 Turtle water dropper

Of miniature size; the opening on the animal's back is ringed with an underglaze floral rosette; covered in a somewhat opaque cream glaze, the base with a putty-coloured biscuit,

L. 9.1 cm.

Mr. Stensan Y. H. Wong

66 Small covered box

With a nipple-like lid-knop. Decorated in underglaze blue with two phoenixes and flaming pearls continuous over box and lid; the glaze with a cream cast, the flat foot with a chalky-white biscuit,

D. 5.9 cm.

Professor and Mrs. K. J. Ratnam

67 Bowl

Of shallow form and with an everted lip; the footrim rather tall; the outer wall decorated in underglaze blue with a chrysanthemum band; the inside mouthrim drawn with summary decorative rings resembling what d'Argencé calls 'couronne de points', the inside bottom with the cursive character for cheng, 正 , sincerity surrounded by a biscuited ring; the under and inner sides of the footrim unglazed, and with a buff-coloured biscuit; the base coated with a chocolate slip,

D. 13.5 cm.

Mr. and Mrs. Frank Lammers

For the exterior décor cf. *Jenyns*, pl. 38A, a bottle bought by the author in Bangkok and attributed by him to "Annam or Siam" *(sic)* and to the 15th century; for the interior, including a closely similar brushed character, cf. *d'Argencé*, pl. 7, no. 16.

68 Jar

Of tall ovoid shape, with 4 ring-handles; the neck with a collar of underglaze-blue lotus-petals; the body with a scroll of 4 peony blooms, and the lower body with 6 lotus panels containing leaf-forms; the under and inner sides of the footrim unglazed, the latter chamfered in to the base, which is coated with a chocolate slip,

Ht 18.1 cm.

The Sinclair Collection

69 Covered box

The lid-top moulded into 8 lobes picked out in underglaze blue in the form of lotus panels, and with a tiny nipple-like knop-handle surrounded by a rosette; the sides of the lid and body with 8 lotus panels containing alternating leaf-forms and wave-pattern; the base recessed, there being no outer side to the footrim, and with a yellowy-cream biscuit,

D. 7.6 cm.

The University of Singapore

70 Covered box

Similar no. 69 but the lid-top not moulded, without knop-handle, and with only 6 lotus panels; the sides of lid and body similarly with 6 lotus panels; the underglaze blue-black pigment dense, and with a 'heaped and piled' effect; the base recessed, with a yellowy-cream biscuit and two dark-brown adhesions,

D. 7.6 cm.

The University of Singapore

71 Miniature covered box

Decorated in a faded underglaze blue with a chrysanthemum spray on the flat top of the lid, and with six vertical panels on the sides of lid and body, containing alternating concentric rhombs and leaf-sprays; the carved foot with a cream-coloured biscuit,

D. 6.6 cm.

Mr. William Willetts

72 Covered box

8-sided; the body and the sides of the lid decorated with 8 panels in underglaze blue featuring alternating lotus rosettes and leaf-sprays; the lid-top with a central *chakra* (or rosette) surrounded by 4 leaf-sprays, outside which are 8 lotus panels; the carved foot with a beige-coloured biscuit,

D. 7.6 cm.

Mr. and Mrs. Frank Lammers

73 Covered box

The lid with a knop in the form of 5 sepals in relief surrounded by a lotus rosette in underglaze blue; the junction between lid and body decorated with a register of broken key-fret pattern; the lower body with a lotus-petal band; the base recessed, and with a greyish-white biscuit,

D. 7.6 cm.

Mr. S. R. Parker

Cf. Dublin, no. 161

74 Covered box

The lid with a nipple-like knop surrounded by a lotus rosette in underglaze blue; the body with an underglaze scroll of 4 lotus blossoms; the base recessed, and with a greyish-white biscuit,

D. 7.5 cm.

Mr. S. R. Parker

75 Jar

Moulded in 6 lobes; with a collar of lotus petals in underglaze blue-black on the shoulder and a scroll of 3 peonies on the body; with 3 cloud-scrolls on lower body; the carved footrim and base with a beige-coloured biscuit,

Ht 6.8 cm.

The University of Singapore

76 Jar

Of flattened globular shape; with a collar of lotus petals in underglaze blue-black on the shoulder, and a scroll of 4 peonies on the body; the lower body with three cloud-scrolls; the carved footrim and recessed base with a beige-coloured biscuit,

Ht 7 cm.

The University of Singapore

77 Jar

Moulded in 8 lobes; with a collar of scalloped petals on the upper shoulder, and on the lower shoulder a band of 4 cloud-scrolls; the body with a scroll comprising 4 peonies; all painted in a bright underglaze Royal blue, with some heaping and piling; the carved footrim and recessed base with a putty-coloured biscuit,

Ht 8.5 cm.

The University of Singapore

78 Bottle

Of flattened globular form and with a tall tubular neck; decorated in underglaze blue with a band of key-fret below the lip, beneath which is a row of 4 suspended trefoils alternating with 4 triangles; the middle neck with a chevron band, backed above and below by a band of 4 alternating trefoils and 4 triangles; the lower neck with a classic scroll, above which the band of trefoils and triangles is repeated; the shoulder with a collar of lotus petals; the body with 4 stylized lotus sprays underneath another band of trefoils and triangles; the lower body with a rosette of upturned lotus petals; the carved footrim of flattened form; the base barely recessed, with an off-white biscuit and one chocolate-brown 'beauty spot',

Ht 18.7 cm.

The Sinclair Collection

79 Dish

With rounded sides, and without mouthrim; decorated in a pale underglaze blue-black, the centre medallion containing a floral spray, the cavetto with two circles of 4 and 8 foliate medallion panels respectively, the medallions also containing floral sprays; set on a background of interlacing trifid forms, cloud-scrolls, and floral half-rosettes; the outside wall with 7 lotus blossoms on a scrolling vine; the footrim unglazed, but the base with a thin oatmeal-coloured glaze,

D. 30.8 cm.

Mr. B. C. Lim

ANNAMESE

Affinities with the Chinese blue-and-white décor suggest the late 14th or early 15th century for no. 79.

80 Stem cup

Of globular form on an elaborately moulded stem and foot, originally with a cover; the body decorated in finely-drawn underglaze blue, with a band of circles between double horizontal lines immediately below the mouth-rim, the circles enclosing diapers with incurved sides: below the circle-band a band of 5-sided lotus panels containing leaf-forms, the points of the panels ending in spirals; the lower body with a band of trefoils above, and a scalloped petal band below; the outer side of the footrim with a chocolate slip; the under and inner sides unglazed, and with a beige-coloured biscuit, the recessed base coated with a chocolate slip,

Ht 17.8 cm.

The Sinclair Collection

A similar stem-cup, covered, and Chinese, is illustrated in *Stockholm*, fig. 33 (Lundgren), and is ascribed to the Hsüan-tê period.

81 Circular covered box

Decorated in underglaze blue; the moulded flat lid with a peony medallion, its sides with 4 ogival medallions containing floral sprays; the sides of the lid and box with classic scroll borders; the lower body with upturned lotus panels enclosing leaf forms; the carved foot with an unglazed base and a light-grey biscuit,

D. 13.8 cm.

Mr. K. T. Goh

The décor combination relates no. 81 to Chinese blue-and-white of the late 14th and early 15th centuries.

82 Kendi

In the shape of a crested gallinaceous bird; the head and tail strongly moulded; the flanged mouth of the vessel with an underglaze-blue rosette of lotus petals; the neck undecorated; the anatomical parts of the bird boldly drawn in underglaze blue with a black tone; all on a milky white slip, and with a translucent glaze; the unglazed flat foot with a putty-coloured biscuit,

Ht (to top of crest) 12.4 cm.

The Sinclair Collection

For a Ming Chinese example, perhaps contemporary, Cf. Maria Penhala, *Far Eastern Ceramics*, The Hague 1963, pl. 21 (Museu Nacional de Arte Antiga, Lisbon), dated to the Chia-ching period.

83 Bottle *(yü hu ch'un-p'ing)*

Of pear-shape; the decoration delicately drawn in underglaze blue, the everted mouthrim with 3 leaf-sprays, the neck with 4 upturned plantain leaves, the shoulder with a diamond diaper band, the body with 4 scrolling lotuses reserved in white, the lower body with 8 upright lotus panels containing leaf-forms; standing on a tall carved foot with a putty-coloured biscuit, and a 'chocolate base',

Ht 27.7 cm.

The Sinclair Collection

84 Bottle *(yü hu ch'un-p'ing)*

Pear-shaped, but moulded into polygonal panels throughout; the tall neck with a foliate mouth, much repaired; the neck with 8 tall panels, each with a floral spray at the top or bottom, the spray alternating with a chequer-board ground, the chequers filled with 4-petalled rosettes; the shoulder and upper body each with 8 hexagonal panels containing alternating floral motives and chequer-board grounds, one of the floral motives being in the form of a bouquet tied with a fillet; the lower body with 8 5-sided lotus panels enclosing leaf-forms,

Ht 27.6 cm.

Mr. K. T. Goh

The décor relates no. 85 to Chinese blue-and-white wares of the late 14th or early 15th centuries.

85 Covered potiche

In the form of a pair of crested gallinaceous birds with moulded heads and tails;

the cover with a simple lid-knop surrounded by a rosette of five scalloped
petals; the anatomical parts picked out
in bright Royal blue; the carved foot
slightly recessed on a flat footrim, unglazed, and with a putty-coloured biscuit,

Ht (to lid knop) 13.1 cm.

The Sinclair Collection

86 Kendi

With neck-flange and mammary spout.
Decorated in underglaze blue, the flange
with a rosette of scalloped petals, the
spout with a peony spray above and
below; the shoulder with a rosette of
cloud collar points; the body with three
peony sprays inside ogival medallions;
all on a wave-patterned ground; the
lower body with a scalloped-petal band,
the flat foot unglazed, and with a putty-
coloured biscuit; some repainting,

Ht 10.9 cm.

The Sinclair Collection

87 Ewer

With tall tubular neck, flanged above,
and with elaborately turned tall handle,
spout, and sticking parts; the body carved
in relief with a pair of birds (? quail)
among scrolling lotuses, the shoulder with
open lotus panels containing half-rosettes
and cloud-scrolls; with a diapered band
on the collar, and two pairs of opposed
lotus panels divided by 3 mouldings towards the top of the neck, opposite the
sticking parts; the flange with a border
of scalloped petals; the carved foot
splayed and with an off-white biscuit;
some repairs,

Ht 20.1 cm.

The Sinclair Collection

For somewhat similar open lotus panels
on a Chinese dish of the 14th century
cf. *Pope II*, pl. 21 (Ardebil 29.48).

88 Dish

Of flattened form. Decorated in underglaze blue, with an interrupted classic
scroll on the flat lip and with a vegetal
spray in the centre medallion; the carved
foot and base with a cream-coloured

biscuit; the glaze with an all-over fine
white crackle, with 6 spur-marks on the
edge of the medallion,

D. 27.6 cm.

The Sinclair Collection

Note a general similarity in design layout
between this and the Sukhothai bowl,
no. 148.

89 Bowl

Of crucible shape. Decorated in underglaze blue with a stylized floral spray
on the inside medallion and an abstract
calligraphic scroll on the upper outside
wall; the flat base with a chocolate slip;
the glaze with an all-over fine white
crackle,

D. 7.9 cm.

Mr. K. T. Goh

As suggested in the Introduction, I con-
sider nos. 88 and 89 as representative
of the very earliest blue-and-whites to
have been made in Annam, contemporary in date with the iron-black range,
and in all likelihood antedating the early
15th-century blue-and-whites by half a
century or more.

90 Jar

Of depressed globular shape, like a fish-
bowl; decorated in underglaze blue-black;
the neck with a collar of scalloped petals,
the body with a scrolling lotus, the lower
body with upturned lotus panels containing leaf-forms; the carved foot with slightly
recessed base, unglazed, and with a putty-
coloured biscuit,

Ht 17.6 cm.

Mr. K. T. Goh

In China the lotus flower was typically
drawn with 16 petals in the late 14th
century, as here. Cf. *Pope I*, pl. 22
(T.K.S. 1377).

91 Jar

Of flattened globular form and with a
wide mouth; the shoulder with a band
of 7 trefoils backed by a beaded border;
the body with four ogival medallions
containing alternating leaf and floral

sprays, and with confronted half-sprays between; the lower body with a ring of upturned lotus petals; the foot flat and with a putty-coloured biscuit; the interior glazed; some repairs,

Ht 10.3 cm.

Mr. K.T. Goh

92 Circular covered bowl *(po kang)*

Of flattened globular form; the body decorated in underglaze blue with a classic scroll below the mouthrim and 4 scrolling peonies on the body; the lower body with a band of scalloped petals; the cover with an inner register of lotus petals around the knop-handle, and an outer register of 4 peony sprays; the foot carved, with a broad shallow footrim, unglazed, and with an oatmeal-coloured biscuit,

Ht (with lid) 13 cm.

The University of Singapore

Cf. no. 36, with a possible attribution to the Hsüan-tê period.

93 Altar vase

Of a graceful baluster shape; decorated in underglaze blue, the neck with a band of diamond-shaped diaper pattern; the shoulder with 6 downturned cloud collar points enclosing half rosettes and cloud-scrolls; the body separated from the neck by 4 circular decorative bands, and featuring a scroll of 4 chrysanthemums; the décor of the lower body separated from the chrysanthemum scroll by 4 circular decorative bands, and comprising 11 tall upturned lotus panels, each enclosing a festooned leaf-form, and measuring almost half the total height of the vase; the under and inner sides of the deep footrim unglazed, and with a putty-coloured biscuit; the recessed foot with a 'chocolate base',

Ht 54 cm.

Mr. K.T. Goh

Cf. the superb no. 3760-1 in the Rijksmuseum voor Volkenkunde, Leiden. It seems probable that such vases are related to a group of inscribed vases with underglaze blue decoration and horizontal mouldings coated with a chocolate slip,

such as are illustrated in *d'Argencé*, pl. XII. These, he says, "viennent se placer en tête de la série des Bat-trang dont ils annoncent les dimensions, la forme, et la decoration." The inscription on one states that it was made at Ba-thuy village, a place in Gia-loc *huyen*, Hai-duong province.

GROUP TWO: ANNAMESE WARES

Family 2. Wares enamelled on the biscuit.

94 Bottle

Presumably originally of *yü hu ch'un-p'ing* shape, but the neck cut down and fitted with a brass collar; enamelled in a dark tomato-red enamel on the biscuit, with a band of lotus petals on the shoulder and a scroll with 2 peonies on the body; the outer side of the foot similarly enamelled; the foot uncarved and with a somewhat concave base; the biscuit a warm sand-colour,

Ht 23.8 cm.

The University of Singapore

95 Vase

Of *kuan* shape and with a high shoulder; the neck and lower body above the foot painted in a dark tomato-red on the biscuit, the shoulder with a band of lotus petals, the body with a scroll of two full-blown peonies, the lower body with two-and-a-half highly convoluted cloud-scrolls; the base markedly concave; the biscuit as in the case of no. 94,

Ht 33.8 cm.

Mr. William Willetts

Compare nos. 94 and 95 with *Flines* pl. 74, no. 1267, a ring-handled jar from Klungkung, Bali, having exactly the same style and subject of decoration, and attributed by de Flines to Tongking and the 15th century. No. 95 is from the Celebes.

GROUP TWO: ANNAMESE WARES

Family 3. Underglaze blue wares, with tomato-red and leaf-green on-glaze enamels.

96 Kendi

Of flattened globular form and with a mammiform spout; the body ribbed; formerly extensively decorated in finely-drawn tomato-red enamel now worn away, and with underglaze-blue figures of two flying birds on the shoulder; the neck-flange with a quatrefoil of scalloped petals; the whole punctuated with dark-brown blobs, originally of leaf-green enamel; the carved foot with a light-grey biscuit,

Ht 11.1 cm.

Mr. K.T. Goh

A gold flanged collar accompanies this piece.

97 Dish

With steep sides and slightly flattened mouthrim; decorated in tomato-red and leaf-green enamels, the former much weakened and the latter tarnished; the centre medallion with a cyprinoid fish among eelgrass, duckweed, and feathery grass, bordered with a scalloped-petal band; the cavetto with a scroll containing 4 lotus flowers; the outside wall with 9 lotus panels enclosing leaf-forms; the carved footrim with a buff-coloured biscuit and the base with a spirally-brushed chocolate slip,

D. 23.9 cm.

The Sinclair Collection

Cf. no. 34 and related pieces. See also *Flines*, pl. 90, no. 1968, Annamese, from Benkoelen.

98 Bowl

In shape like a flattened globular almsbowl with a wide mouth and raised mouthrim; the foot without footrim, the base recessed and of 'hole-bottom' type, covered with a chocolate slip; the shoulder, body and lower body decorated with a system of cloud collar points in underglaze blue, leaf-green and tomato-red; the body with 6 ogival medallions containing small birds with wings outstretched; re-painted,

Ht 15.2 cm.

Mr. K.T. Goh

99 Dish

With steep sides, flattened rim and raised edge; decorated in underglaze blue, and with overglaze leaf-green and tomato-red enamels (mainly repainted) the centre medallion featuring a bird (perhaps a starling) on a branch of fruiting lychees, surrounded by a border of scalloped petals; the inside wall with stylised chrysanthemum and peony scrolls; the outside wall with 9 lotus panels enclosing leaf-forms; the carved foot with a warm buff biscuit, and the base with traces of a spirally applied glaze,

D. 32.2 cm.

Mr. K.T. Goh

On the analogy of *Pope II*, pl. 57 (an Annamese dish) no. 75 may be dated to the mid-15th century; *Pope II*, pl. 41, illustrates a Chinese blue-and-white dish featuring fruiting lychees dated to the early 15th-century. See further *Flines* pl. 90, no. 1968, Annamese, from Benkoelen.

GROUP TWO: ANNAMESE WARES

Family 4. Underglaze iron-black wares.

100 Bottle *(yü hu ch'un-p'ing)*

Pear-shaped; decorated in underglaze black on a cream ground, the flared neck with 3 upturned plantain leaves, the shoulder with three lotus panels containing (1) a flaming pearl, (2) a brocaded ball, and (3) a motive comprising a curved sail-like triangular form surrounded by 5 spirals; the body with a scroll comprising 3 chrysanthemum blooms; the lower body with 5 lotus panels enclosing leaf-forms; the carved and splayed footrim unglazed and with a beige-coloured biscuit; the recessed foot with a 'chocolate base',

Ht 29.6 cm.

The Sinclair Collection

101 Beaker

Of bowed shape, chamfered in to a flat foot; with a decorative calligraphic scroll in underglaze iron-black summarily drawn on the upper part of the body; an oatmeal glaze within and without, and 5 spur-marks on the inside bottom,

Max. d. 10 cm.

Mr. William Willetts

102 Bowl

With everted mouth; decorated in underglaze iron-black, the centre medallion with a floral spray, the inside mouthrim with a classic scroll, the outside wall with an abstract calligraphic scroll; all covered with a translucent gum-coloured glaze; the carved footrim with a buff-coloured biscuit and the base with a 'chocolate bottom',

D. 14.1 cm.

Mr. and Mrs. E. M. T. Lu

103 Beaker

Of bowed profile chamfered in to a carved foot, with a barely recessed base; the decorative calligraphic scroll in underglaze iron-black summarily drawn, but with a superb pristine translucent glaze inside and out; with 5 spur-marks on the inside bottom,

D. 12 cm.

Mr. and Mrs. Frank Lammers

104 Beaker

Of bowed shape, chamfered in to a carved foot with a wide, flat footrim; the body with a smudged finely-drawn decorative calligraphic scroll in underglaze iron-black between two pairs of roughly-drawn horizontal bands; with a finely crackled oatmeal glaze inside and out; 5 spur-marks on the inside bottom; repaired,

Max. d. 14.7 cm.

Mr. William Willetts

105 Beaker

Of bowed shape, chamfered in to a carved foot with a wide footrim, the base barely recessed and with a beige-coloured biscuit; the body with a decorative calligraphic scroll, finely drawn; with a finely crackled oatmeal glaze inside and out,

and with 5 spur-marks on the inside bottom,

D. 13.3 cm.

The University of Singapore

For purity of form no. 105 leads the group that contains nos. 101, 103 and 104; compare with them *Okuda*, fig. 25.

106 Saucer-dish

With iron-black underglaze decoration on an off-white biscuit, largely covered with a gum-coloured translucent glaze; the inside medallion with a dissolved floral spray, the outside wall with an equally summary calligraphic scroll; the foot carved and the base *bisqué*,

D. 14.7 cm.

Mr. S. R. Parker

107 Jar

Roughly potted, with a slack mouthrim, and low, sagging shoulder; ornamented on the shoulder with three iron-black vegetal sprays; with a cream glaze, finely crackled, and an off-white, slightly pinkish biscuit; the foot flat and without footrim,

Ht 7.1 cm.

Mr. Stensan Y. H. Wong

108 Bowl

With everted mouth; decorated in underglaze iron-black, the ringed centre medallion with a floral spray, the inside mouthrim with a summary decorative band, the outside body with a roughly-executed decorative calligraphic band; all covered by a finely-crackled gum-like and translucent glaze; the carved footrim with a cream-coloured biscuit, and the base with a chocolate slip,

D. 16.6 cm.

The University of Singapore

109 Bowl

With everted lip; the design drawn in underglaze iron-black on a light grey body, with a floral spray in the centre medallion, a classic scroll border similar to that of no. 88 on the inside mouthrim,

43

and an abstract calligraphic scroll on the outside wall; the cream glaze stained with an orange cast; the carved foot unglazed,

D. 25 cm.

Mr. K. T. Goh

110 Bowl

Boldly decorated in underglaze iron-black with a classic scroll on the upper inside wall and a vegetal spray on the medallion; the outside wall with a freely drawn abstract calligraphic scroll; the iron much crystallised and with many deep sienna 'rust' marks; the foot unglazed, the inner side of the foot and base with a chocolate slip,

D. 16.9 cm.

The Sinclair Collection

GROUP TWO: ANNAMESE WARES

Family 5. Cream-glazed monochromes.

111 Bowl

Of crucible form, the mouth inverted; with a dull crackled gum-coloured glaze inside and out; the carved shallow foot with a beige-coloured biscuit, and covered with a 'chocolate slip',

Ht 8.2 cm.

The University of Singapore

112 Saucer-dish

With scalloped rim; the inside wall with a roughly drawn relief pattern; the inside medallion with some indication of a moulded pattern, outside which are 5 spur-marks; with a translucent gum-coloured glaze; the footrim roughly carved and with an off-white biscuit,

D. 14.1 cm.

Mr. and Mrs. Trevor Rutter

113 Bowl

On a high footrim, and with an everted mouth; with a block-moulded floral decoration on the lower inside wall; all covered with a fine gum-coloured glaze,

minutely crackled; the carved foot with an off-white biscuit,

D. 12 cm.

Mr. and Mrs. E. M. T. Lu

114 Jarlet

Of flat globular form; covered with a cream glaze stained a slight orange; the lower body and carved foot unglazed, and with a pale grey biscuit,

Ht 4.1 cm.

Mr. and Mrs. Frank Lammers

115 Beaker

With slightly everted lip; the body decorated with shallow gouged vertical ribs covered with a gum-coloured translucent glaze; the carved footrim of flat 'T'ang' type, and with a chamfered outer side; the foot unglazed, with an oatmeal-coloured biscuit; the inside glazed, and with 5 spur-marks,

D. 16.2 cm.

The Sinclair Collection

116 Bowl

Of beaker shape; the outside wall with an incised continuous vegetal scroll; covered outside and inside with a pale olive-grey glaze; the inside bottom with 5 spur-marks; the carved foot with a finely granular pinkish-grey biscuit; repaired,

Max. d. of mouth 18.7 cm.

Mr. William Willetts

GROUP TWO: ANNAMESE WARES

Family 6. Copper-green glazed wares.

117 Beaker

Of bowed form, the body chamfered in to the foot; on the body a roughly-incised floral scroll, set against three incised double horizontal decorative bands; with an apple-green copper glaze inside and out, running in rills on the chamfered lower body, with a biscuited ring on the inside bottom; with the high carved footrim and base unglazed, and with a putty-coloured biscuit; old vertical cracks,

Ht 11.2 cm.

The University of Singapore

118 Beaker

Of deep bowl-shape, the mouthrim slightly everted; the lower body chamfered in to the foot; the body with an incised floral scroll between two pairs of incised horizontal decorative bands; with a mottled apple-green copper glaze inside and out, and with a biscuited ring on the inside bottom; the high carved footrim and foot unglazed, and with a putty-coloured biscuit; repaired,

Ht 11.4 cm.

Mr. William Willetts

119 Beaker

Of bowed form, the lower body chamfered in to the foot; with a double carved horizontal decorative band on the upper body; with an apple-green copper glaze inside and outside, and a biscuited ring on the inside bottom; the high carved footrim and recessed foot unglazed, and with a putty-coloured biscuit,

Ht 9.2 cm.

Mr. William Willetts

120 Beaker

Of bowed form, with slightly everted lip, the lower body chamfered in to the foot; with an apple-green copper glaze, somewhat abraded and having a bluish tinge; with an irregular biscuited ring on the inside bottom and spirally-incised wreathing marks on the outside; the high carved foot unglazed, and with a putty-coloured biscuit,

Ht 8.7 cm.

The University of Singapore

121 Jarlet

Of flattened globular form; the body moulded into 7 vertical lobes and covered with an olive-green copper glaze; the

flat foot with a buff biscuit and some brownish oxidation flushes,

Ht 5 cm.

The University of Singapore

122 Covered box

The lid and box with thickened rims; with a thin pale apple-green copper glaze; the carved foot with a wide, flat footrim and buff-coloured biscuit,

D 7.9 cm.

Mr. and Mrs. E. M. T. Lu

123 Jarlet

Of flattened globular form; the body, with six moulded vertical lobes, covered with a dark-green matt copper glaze and with an adhesion spot; the foot with a buff biscuit, the footrim carved,

Ht 4.3 cm.

Mr. and Mrs. Trevor Rutter

124 Bowl

Of cup-shape, with vertical ribs; with an apple-green glaze on the outer wall, abraded on the spines of the vertical ribs; with a warm creamy glaze on the inside of the bowl; the carved foot standing on a tall footrim, with a distinct recess cut between the outer side of the foot and lower body, the former with two horizontal bands of chocolate slip; the under and inner sides of the foot and the flat base with a cream biscuit,

D. 10.4 cm.

Mr. and Mrs. E. M. T. Lu

125 Bowl

Similar to no. 124; with a somewhat degraded apple-green glaze on the outside wall, the outer side of the footrim, and the base, and with a degraded opalescent-white glaze on the inside of the bowl; with an off-white biscuit beneath the glaze and on the carved footrim,

D. 9.6 cm.

Mr. William Willetts

126 Saucer-dish

With a slightly flattened mouthrim; covered in a mottled dark apple-green copper glaze, but for a biscuited ring around the centre medallion, parts of the lower body, and the carved foot; the footrim slightly splayed; the biscuit of an oatmeal colour,

D. 16.5 cm.

The University of Singapore

An illustration of the foot appears on p. 191, upper right; an almost identical foot is featured in *Locsin* p. 227, pl. 161, from Mindoro.

127 Bowl

Cup-shaped and similar to nos. 124 and 125; a recess separates the lower body from the high footrim; the body covered with a soft pale olive-green copper glaze inside and out, as also the base; the unglazed footrim with a buff-coloured biscuit,

Mr. and Mrs. E. M. T. Lu

128 Jarlet

Of globular form, the body with 8 moulded vertical lobes; covered with a deep green copper glaze; the carved foot unglazed and with a buff biscuit,

Ht 6.8 cm.

Mr. K. T. Goh

Cf. nos. 121, 123.

129 Bowl

Of cup-shape, and similar to nos. 124, 125 and 127; the foot with a recess between it and the lower body, the outer footrim coated with a chocolate slip; the body with delicately moulded vertical striations, their upper ends sharpened by incised lines to represent lotus-leaf fluting; the inside and outside covered with an apple-green copper glaze, somewhat worn on the outside, and with a 'chocolate base',

D. 9.8 cm.

Mr. J. W. van Baak

130 Saucer-dish

With flattened rim; a ring of biscuit around the centre medallion; parts of the lower body and the carved foot unglazed, and with a putty-coloured biscuit; the inside and outside walls covered with a mottled pale apple-green copper glaze,

D. 18.1 cm.

Mr. and Mrs. E. M. T. Lu

131 Covered box

Of flattened form, similar to no. 122; with an apple-green copper glaze on cover and box, largely flaked off the latter; the carved foot unglazed, and with a 'chocolate base',

D. 7.1 cm.

Mr. and Mrs. Frank Lammers

132 Jar

Of an unusual pear-shape, the shoulder squared-off above, so forming a flat frame enclosing the rimless mouth; the top and angles of the shoulder with a splashed apple-green copper glaze; between the splashes four underglaze-blue forms resembling thistle-heads; the lower body with a band of upturned lotus petals; the unglazed foot without a footrim, and with a cream-coloured biscuit,

Ht 9.2 cm.

The Sinclair Collection

According to an informant the jar exhibits features of several fruits, having the squared-off proximal end of Barringtonia, the frilly sepals of Passiflora, and the general form of an aubergine.

133 Bowl

Deep, and with an everted rim; decorated inside with a pattern of scalloped petals and spirally radiating cloud-pattern and combed forms; with a broad circle of biscuit surrounding the centre medallion; the rim regularly nicked; covered with a matt and somewhat worn apple-green copper-glaze; the lower body and carved footrim unglazed and with a putty-coloured biscuit; the inside of the footrim and flat base with a chocolate slip, D. 18.2 cm.

The Sinclair Collection

A somewhat similar bowl is illustrated in Okuda, fig. 18.

GROUP TWO: ANNAMESE WARES

Family 7. Brown-glazed wares.

134 Bowl

With slightly everted rim; the inside wall having a moulded pattern of vertical bifid lines and a circular biscuited ring; the body covered with a mottled caramel glaze; the carved foot with a buff-coloured biscuit,

D. 16 cm.

Mr. and Mrs. E. M. T. Lu

135 Bowl

Similar to no. 134, but with a dark chocolate glaze, the centre medallion having a distinct greenish tinge; the lower body, carved footrim, and base unglazed, and with a putty-coloured biscuit,

D. 16.1 cm.

Mr. K. T. Goh

136 Bowl

Similar to nos. 134 and 135, but without ornamentation; the lower body, carved footrim and base with a brownish-grey biscuit,

D. 16.9 cm.

The Sinclair Collection

By their formal relationship with the saucer-dishes nos. 126 and 130, these bowls (with no. 146) proclaim themselves as Annamese, and so help to establish the identity of the group containing nos. 138, 139, 140, 141, 142, 143 and 144.

137 Beaker

With a slightly everted rim, the body chamfered in to a high carved footrim; covered in a rich chestnut-brown glaze; with a biscuited ring on the inside bottom;

the lower body and foot unglazed, and with a bright beige-coloured biscuit,

Ht 8.2 cm.

Mr. and Mrs. E. M. T. Lu

The relationship between no. 137 and the green-glazed beakers 117, 118, 119 and 120 will be remarked; it is closer than that between these and the flat-bottomed iron-black series, nos. 101, 103, 104 and 105.

138 Beaker

With everted mouthrim, the sides vertical and caved slightly inwards; the inside and upper outside walls with a patchy light-brown glaze, like shellac, the lower body and carved foot with a brownish-grey biscuit,

Ht 7.6 cm.

Mr. William Willetts

139 Jar

Of flattened globular form, with a short neck and narrow mouth; with 2 incised decorative circular bands on the shoulder; covered in a caramel-coloured glaze; the lower body and carved foot unglazed, and with an ochre-coloured biscuit; the inner side of the foot chamfered down to the base,

Ht 8.7 cm.

The University of Singapore

140 Jar

Of ovoid form with a high shoulder; covered in a dark toffee-coloured glaze, the lower body and carved foot with a pale brick-red biscuit,

Ht 8.4 cm.

The University of Singapore

141 Kendi or water dropper

Enclosed above, and with an S-shaped *appliqué* handle representing a snake; a circular hole has been bored through the shoulder to serve as a vent; covered in a mottled caramel-coloured glaze; the lower body and carved foot with a bright pink, almost vermillion biscuit; the inner side of the footrim chamfered down to the base,

Ht (to top of handle) 9 cm.

The Sinclair Collection

142 Platelet

Of flattened form, the rim slightly everted; covered in a caramel-coloured glaze; the lower outside wall and carved foot unglazed, and with a grey biscuit having a pinkish tinge near the glaze boundaries and inside the foot,

D. 11.4 cm.

The Sinclair Collection

143 Bottle

Of *yü hu ch'un p'ing* shape; the body covered with a matt iron-brown glaze of a dark toffee colour; the lower body and foot with a grey biscuit having pink flushes; the outer side of the footrim splayed outwards above, and inwards below; the inner side of the footrim partly chamfered down,

Ht 27.5 cm.

The Sinclair Collection

144 Bottle

Similar in shape to no. 143 but smaller; with 3 decorative circular bands on the shoulder and 3 others on the lower body; covered with a dark caramel-coloured glaze; the lower body and foot with a light brick biscuit; the footrim similar to that of no. 139,

Ht 23.2 cm.

The University of Singapore

A bottle similar to nos. 143 and 144 is illustrated in *Locsin*, pl. 112, from Mindoro.

145 Saucer-dish

With slightly everted rim; a ring of biscuit round the centre medallion; parts of the lower body and foot unglazed, and with a putty-coloured biscuit; the inside and outside walls with a thin, pale brown glaze irregularly applied; the carved foot with its inner side chamfered down to the base,

D. 16 cm.

Mr. William Willetts

It is the similarity of such pieces as no. 145 to the green-glazed variety (nos. 126 and 130) that prompts the belief that all these brown-glazed wares (i.e. nos. 138-145) are Annamese; they are at least fairly consistant as a group.

146 Bowl

With everted mouthrim, and standing on a high narrow foot; with a worn tan-coloured glaze outside and a duck-egg blue glaze inside, and with a biscuited ring around the centre medallion; the footrim and base partially unglazed, and with a light-brown biscuit,

D. 17.8 cm.

The University of Singapore

147 Ornament

In the form of a lion dog *(shih tzŭ)*, the features strongly moulded, and with a dark-brown chocolate glaze,

L. 20.6 cm.

The University of Singapore

This ornament was excavated at Kota Tinggi, Malaysia, in 1955 and may perhaps be dated to the 16th century. By a comparison with *Okuda*, fig. 22, illustrating an ewer in the shape of a dolphin of the type called in Japan *ame-kōchi-yū*, "caramel [of] Cochin [China] glaze" (Kochi being the name given by the Japanese to the ancient Vietnam from the beginning of the Sung), its Annamese credentials are perhaps established.

GROUP THREE: SUKHOTHAI WARES

148 Bowl

Of flattened form; cleanly decorated in underglaze black, the centre medallion with a fragmented curvilinear scroll, the lip with a chevron band, the outer wall with a debased floral scroll; painted on a white slip, and covered with a warm reddish-cream translucent glaze; the carved foot with a granular grey biscuit containing whitish particles,

D. 29.3 cm.

Mr. and Mrs. E. M. T. Lu

There are clear indications of some sort of relationship between the kilns of Sukhothai and those of Annam. It is especially evident when we compare the Sukhothai underglaze iron-black range (e.g. no. 148) with that of Annam (nos. 108, 109), as also with related Annamese underglaze-blue wares such as no. 88. In distinguishing between the two groups one criterion is decisive - paste.

149 Bowl

Decorated in underglaze iron-black on a white slip; with 3 circular decorative bands on the upper inside wall and 3 more surrounding the centre medallion; the inside wall with 16 rosettes or sun-bursts, the medallion with 7 rosettes surrounding a central wide-sided circular band; the outside wall with 14 rosettes between two pairs of circular decorative bands; the carved foot with a grey-brown granular biscuit containing white particles,

D. 14.2 cm.

Mr. K. T. Goh

It might be fanciful to suggest an actual relationship between this type of décor and that found on Chi Chou *temmokus* such as one illustrated in *Chinese Ceramics* (Nihon Keizai Shimbum-Sha), Tokyo 1960, fig. 60 (Miyawaki); on the other hand it might not. Cf. *Spinks I*, fig. 11, middle (Djakarta), Sukhothai, from Bali; cf. also *Ram*, pl. 29, in which he illustrates three closely-similar bowls allegedly from the three separate kiln-sites of Sukhothai, Sawankoloke and Kalong. I have my doubts about this. But at least the sunburst motive travelled as far as Sawankoloke; cf. no. 177.

150 Bowl

Painted in underglaze iron-black on a cream slip, the glaze totally eroded; with 5 concentric decorative bands on the upper inside wall, the middle band regularly interrupted by oblique lines

scratched through to the slip; the lower inside wall with 6 panels, each containing a *monkut*, or 'tiered crown', alternating with 6 vertical bands of 'comma' pattern flanked by triangles made up of rammifying lines; with the centre medallion surrounded by 3 broad circular decorative bands, and containing a *cakra* or solar whorl with 5 spur-marks at its edge; the outside wall repeating the main motive of the inside wall; the carved foot with a pale brown gritty biscuit containing whitish particles,

D. 20 cm.

The Sinclair Collection

The resemblance between this type of centre medallion and that of the Annamese copper-green bowl no. 133 should be noted.

151 Bottle

Of *yü hu ch'un p'ing* shape; with underglaze iron-black decoration in the form of a vegetal scroll containing 4 prominent broad leaf-forms round the upper body, with 2 circular decorative bands above it and 3 below; the flared neck with a rough pattern of pendent and upturned leaf-forms; all on a white slip covered by a translucent glaze; the carved foot unglazed, and with a granular dark-grey biscuit; the neck repaired,

Ht 27.9 cm.

Mr. K. T. Goh

The pendent leaf-forms may perhaps be related to those of no. 132. The broad leaf-forms are characteristic of Sukhothai cf. *Spinks I*, figs. 8 and 10, left), and pass into the Sawankoloke repertory. Shape-relations between this Sukhothai piece (and no. 153) and the Annamese version, nos. 60, 83, 84 and 100, are close indeed.

152 Vase

Ok *kuan* shape, but with sides sloping steeply in towards the foot from a high and wide shoulder; covered in an iron-black underglaze decoration comprising three peony scrolls bounded above and below by circular decorative bands, all on a pink slip; the carved foot largely unglazed, and with a gritty grey-brown biscuit containing white particles,

Ht 15.6 cm.

The Sinclair Collection

The Tzŭ Chou influence would seem to be especially strong in this piece.

153   Bottle

Of *yü hu ch'un p'ing* shape; with a boldly executed abstract design of vegetal or calligraphic origin contained in 3 panels on the body and confined within 2 pairs of decorative circular bands; painted on a cream slip under a patchy transparent glaze; the carved foot with a sand-coloured gritty biscuit containing whitish particles; the lip repaired,

Ht 25.3 cm.

The University of Singapore

Compare both this and no. 151 with *Spinks I*, fig. 4, middle (Djakarta), Suk-hothai, found at Acheh, Sumatra.

154   Bowl

Similar in form to no. 150, but with a somewhat simplified and more legible décor, painted on a dull cream slip under a well-preserved transparent glaze, and with 5 spur-marks at the edge of the cer.tre medallion; the carved foot with a rough pale-brown gritty biscuit having whitish inclusions,

Max. d. 21.6 cm.

The University of Singapore

155   Bowl

Similar in form to nos. 150 and 154 but a size smaller; neatly potted and with an even simpler and more legible décor inside and out; painted on a dull cream slip, the glaze totally eroded; with 5 barely visible spur-marks on the centre medallion; the carved foot with a bright brown biscuit containing whitish particles,

D. 13.7 cm.

The University of Singapore

Compare *Spinks I*, fig. 10, right; also nos. 158 and 160.

156   Bowl

Closely similar in form to no. 150, but with a well-integrated transparent straw-coloured glaze; the lower body near the foot free from glaze, as also the carved footrim and base; with a grey-brown gritty biscuit containing whitish particles; the base with a chocolate-brown 'beauty spot',

Max. d. 20.5 cm.

The University of Singapore

157   Jar

Of squat globular form; the shoulder and upper body decorated with an abstract curvilinear pattern in iron-black between horizontal decorative bands on a white slip; all covered wit.ı a thin translucent glaze, partly deteriorated; the crudely-carved foot with a light-brown gritty biscuit containing whitish particles,

Ht 9.5 cm.

Mr. and Mrs. E. M. T. Lu

The decoration, crude though it is, is reminiscent of the 'calligraphic' scroll of the Annamese iron-black group. For a similar piece cf. *Spinks I*, fig. 22, right (Djakarta), from Acheh, described therein as Sawankoloke. Cf. also *Spinks I*, fig. 44, left (Djakarta), from Acheh, also des-cribed as Sawankoloke, which has ring-handles but the identical décor.

158   Bowl

Similar to no. 155, but with the tiered crown motive more conspicuous around the centre medallion, and replaced on the outside wall by a decorative band of curved oblique brush-strokes; 5 spur-marks on the edge of the centre medallion; the glaze deteriorated; the carved foot with a grey-brown biscuit containing whitish particles,

D. 12.7 cm.

Mr. and Mrs. E. M. T. Lu

159   Bowl

Of similar décor to no. 155, but lacking the ring of tiered crowns around the centre medallion; the somewhat opaque whitish glaze well integrated; the roughly carved foot with a grey-brown biscuit containing whitish particles,

D. 18.7 cm.

Mr. S. R. Parker

160 Bowl

Closely similar in all respects to no. 155, but less well preserved, the slip with a yellowish tinge and the biscuit exposed along the mouthrim,

D. 15.6 cm.

The University of Singapore

For an illustration of the foot see p. 191, lower left.

161 Sherd

Comprising the centre portion of a bowl such as nos. 150, 154, 155, 156, 158, 159,

Max. d. 18.1 cm.

The University of Singapore

From the Thuriang kiln site, Sukhothai,

162 Dish

The flattened mouthrim painted in underglaze iron-black with two interrupted decorative bands; the inside wall laid with a cream slip; the cavetto with a fruiting vegetal scroll in iron-black, and the centre medallion with a fish; 5 spurmarks are partly concealed by the mottled body of the fish; all covered by a somewhat opaque milky-white glaze giving a lustred appearance; the outside wall slipped and glazed, and with 2 iron-black decorative bands; the carved foot with a light grey-brown biscuit containing whitish granules,

D. 27 cm.

The University of Singapore

Compare *Spinks I*, fig. 10, left, a Sukhothai dish found in Bali.

163 Dish

The flattened mouthrim with several roughly drawn circular bands in underglaze iron black; the centre medallion with a fish, above which is what appears to be the beginning of a floral spray

of Annamese type (e.g. no. 109), as though the artist had changed his mind; with 5 spur-marks inside the medallion; the outside wall with a girdle of roughly-drawn decorative bands; all on a cream slip covered by a thin translucent glaze; the carved foot showing a granular, brownish-red biscuit, grey at the edges, with whitish granules in the matrix,

D. 25.7 cm.

The Sinclair Collection

164 Dish

Of conical form, the flattened mouthrim and the outside wall with circular decorative underglaze iron-black bands; the centre medallion with a fish, mottled, and thereby camouflaging the 5 spur-marks; drawn on a cream biscuit and covered by a pitted thin transparent glaze; the carved foot with a brownish-pink biscuit containing whitish particles,

D. 25.4 cm.

The University of Singapore

165 Dish

Of conical form, the flattened mouthrim with a decorative band in underglaze iron-black based on a motive of 3 brushstrokes, two curved and partly enclosing the third, which is shorter and straight; the centre medallion with a fish among water-weeds; the outside wall with an abstract calligraphic scroll; all on a cream slip, and covered with a translucent finely-crackled glaze, stained over much of its surface in a warmish orange tinge; the carved foot partly covered in slip, and partly revealing a greyish-brown gritty biscuit,

D. 27.9 cm.

The Sinclair Collection

A similar mouthrim decoration may be seen on dishes illustrated in *Spinks I*, figs. 6 and 7, both Sukhothai; it is not dissimilar to that of no. 148.

166 Dish

With everted lip; the inside and outside walls slipped and glazed, the lip with 3 decorative bands in underglaze iron-black, the outside wall with 3 similar bands; the centre medallion with a fish and 5 spur-marks; the carved foot with a terracotta biscuit containing white particles,

D. 25.8 cm.

The University of Singapore

167 Dish

With a flat lip, the inside laid with a cream slip; the centre medallion with a fish in underglaze iron-black irregularly mottled, and so concealing 5 spur-marks within the medallion; all covered with a translucent glaze; the outside wall with a slip and two decorative circular bands in iron-black, but unglazed; the roughly carved foot unglazed, and with a coarse grey-brown biscuit containing white particles,

D. 26 cm.

The University of Singapore

168 Bowl

With somewhat flattened mouthrim decorated with 3 circular iron-black decorative bands; the centre medallion, ringed by two decorative bands, containing a well-drawn fish, its mottled body helping to camouflage 5 spur-marks; all on a cream slip; the outside wall similarly slipped, and with 3 decorative bands, but unglazed; the carved foot with a dark-brown biscuit containing whitish granules, and with a well-defined cylindrical pontil mark on the base, the biscuit of a lighter hue within the mark; the piece exceptionally well potted,

D. 22.9 cm.

The University of Singapore

The cylindrical pontil mark is exceptional on a Sukhothai piece, and must indicate that the bowl stood at the bottom of the stack. If the deduction is correct then it disposes of a widely-accepted view that the pots were fired inverted. For an illustration of the foot see p. 191, lower right.

169 Sherd

Comprising the centre medallion of a

dish or bowl such as nos. 162, 163, 164, 165, 166, 167 and 168; a flat disc-shaped pontil with 5 spurs adheres to the carved foot,

Max. d. 18.3 cm.

The University of Singapore

From the Thuriang kiln site, Sukhothai.

170 Sherd

Similar to no. 169 but without the disc-shaped pontil, or any vestige of spur-marks within the centre medallion,

Max. d. 16.7 cm.

Mr. and Mrs. Frank Lammers

From the Thuriang kiln site, Sukhothai.

171 Sherd

Similar to nos. 169 and 170, and with 5 spur-marks within the medallion,

Max. d. 15.2 cm.

Mr. and Mrs. Frank Lammers

From the Thuriang kiln site, Sukhothai.

GROUP FOUR: SAWANKOLOKE WARES

Family 1. Wares decorated in underglaze iron-black.

172 Bowl

With everted lip, decorated in underglaze iron-black on a dull white slip; the interior with a centre medallion featuring a five-pointed star and surrounded by 13 triangular rays filled with vertical hatching; the outside wall with a register of 7 tiered crowns; all covered in a transparent celadon-type glaze with a fine white fish-roe crackle; the lower body and carved foot unglazed, and with a coarse reddish-brown biscuit containing whitish granules,

D. 14.8 cm.

Dr. D. Stevens

The décor and the coarse biscuit point to Sukhothai, whereas the celadon-type glaze suggests Sawankoloke. There is no indication of a cylindrical pontil. This bowl, together with nos. 173, 174, 175, 176, may perhaps be considered as very early Sawankoloke ware. For a some-what similar centre medallion on the cover of a Sukhothai bowl see *Spinks II*, fig. 3, bottom (Ladejinsky); yet this is really a variant of the tiered-crown motive. For an illustration of the foot see p. 192, upper left.

173   Bowl

With everted lip, decorated in underglaze iron-black painted directly on the body; the centre medallion with the 'double vajra' motive, and the cavetto with a degenerated vegetal scroll featuring 4 prominent broad leaf-forms as in no. 151; the outside wall with four figures each composed of several superimposed and symmetrically-opposed paired upcurved brush-strokes, as it were resembling the branches of a fir tree; covered in a transparent greenish celadon glaze with a fine white crackle; the lower body and carved foot with a well-levigated bright pink, almost orange, biscuit,

D. 13.6 cm.

Mr. William Willetts

No. 173 also illustrates an apparent transitional phase, which could well be mistaken for Sukhothai. The vegetal scroll with prominent broad leaf-forms (for which see no. 151) and the band of 'fir-trees' (reminiscent of the tiered-crown motive), suggest Sukhothai. The celadon glaze with white-veined crackle, the superior biscuit, and the neatly carved foot point to Sawankoloke; there is however no indication of the use of a pontil. Cf. *Spinks II*, fig. 7, top (Phya Buranasiri Bongsa), which Spinks calls Sawankoloke; also *Diskul I*, p. 12, where an apparently identical piece is featured as Sukhothai. A third piece, featuring the 'double-vajra' centre medallion and illustrated in *Ram*, pl. 28, middle row, right, is from the Kalong kiln.

174   Bowl

With everted rim; decorated in underglaze iron-black, the centre medallion with a summary vegetal form inside 3 thick con-centric bands, the cavetto below the mouthrim with a band of figures each made up of 3 or 4 superimposed curved brush-strokes; the outside wall with 5 figures similar to those on no. 173 between circular decorative bands; all covered in a greenish celadon glaze with a fine white crackle; the carefully carved foot having a pink biscuit; the base with a central grey area, distinctly suggesting the use of the cylindrical pontil,

D. 12.8 cm.

The University of Singapore

The glaze with its white-veined crackle connects this piece to nos. 172 and 173 while the 'fir-tree' motive relates it parti-cularly to 173; so does the biscuit and the neat potting.

175   Bowl

With everted rim; decorated in underglaze iron-black on a grey slip, the centre medallion with a spiral vegetal scroll inside circular bands, the cavetto below the mouthrim with a band of figures similar to those in the same position on no. 174; the outside wall with a vegetal scroll between decorative bands; covered in a glassy, translucent, crackled celadon glaze; the lower body with some exposed traces of an underglaze iron-brown pig-ment, and the outer side of the foot recessed above, and partly covered with an iron-brown slip, as in the Annamese examples nos. 124 and 129; the carved foot with a pale pink biscuit, and with traces of a cylindrical pontil on the base,

D. 12.8 cm.

Professor and Mrs. K. J. Ratnam

Here again is a transitional piece. The vegetal scroll on the outside wall re-sembles those featured on nos. 151 and 173, while the figured band on the cavetto below the mouthrim occurs also on no. 174; these may be residual Suk-hothai features. Glaze, biscuit, and pot-ting-technique point to Sawankoloke.

176   Vase

With wide body, trumpet-shaped neck, and wide flared mouth; decorated in underglaze iron-black with 7 circular bands on the shoulder and 3 on the lower body, between which is a continuous vegetal scroll having prominent broad leaf-forms;

covered with a translucent glaze having a fine white crackle; the lower body and carved foot unglazed, with a pinkish-grey biscuit, and with clear indications of a cylindrical pontil,

Ht 13.1 cm.

Mr. K. T. Goh

The vegetal scroll resembles that of no. 151, while the appearance of the foot is similar to that of nos. 173, 174 and 175. No. 176 is undoubtedly Sawankoloke, but perhaps very early Sawankoloke.

177 Bottle

Of *yü hu ch'un p'ing* shape, but with a cup-like mouth (restored); painted in iron-black directly on the body with 3 series of circular decorative bands of varying thicknesses alternating with two registers of rosettes or sun-bursts, the upper register with one row, the lower with three; all covered in a translucent, crackled, gum-coloured glaze; the lower body and neatly carved foot with brownish-grey biscuit, and the base with a circular pontil scar,

Ht 20 cm.

The University of Singapore

The décor, similar to that of no. 149, suggests that this is an early Sawankoloke piece, reflecting the influence of Sukhothai. For a similar shape see *Spinks I*, fig. 55, left (Djakarta), described as Sawankoloke, from western Sulawesi; and for a similar décor on a Sawankoloke wide-mouthed vase, in shape similar to no. 177, see *Ram*, pl. 42(c). While preparing the present catalogue the writer has also come across a Sawankoloke covered box featuring sun-bursts, and another with the "fir-tree" motive. Both pieces are covered with a greenish celadon-type glaze, having the fine white-veined crackle characteristic of most of the foregoing vessels.

178 Bottle

Of ovoid shape and with a cup-shaped mouth; unglazed, but boldly painted in iron-black on a smooth warm biscuit-coloured slip in 3 registers, with horizontal circular decorative bands between: on the upper shoulder, a row of upright

pyramids of 6 or more wedge-shaped brush-strokes, a form conceivably based on that of the Khmer *prasat* or sanctuary-tower; on the lower shoulder, a horizontal band made up of sets of 4 superimposed brush-strokes resembling those on nos. 174 and 175; on the body, confronting half-rosettes with festoons of wedge-shaped brush-strokes at their apices; the carved foot with a buff-coloured biscuit and clear pontil scar,

Ht 21.9 cm.

The Sinclair Collection

There are obvious affinities to Sukhothai in this décor, yet the piece is unquestionably Sawankoloke; cf. no. 177.

179 Bottle

Of depressed globular shape, and with a cup-shaped mouth; painted in iron-black on a grey slip with a vegetal scroll on the body between two rows of horizontal circular bands; the glaze almost entirely eroded; the neatly carved foot with a pink biscuit, and traces of a pontil mark, Ht 10.2 cm.

The University of Singapore

Again the vegetal scroll relates no. 179 to examples such as nos. 151, 173, 175 and 176.

180 Bottle

Of depressed globular shape, with a cup-shaped mouth and moulded shoulder, and with 2 circular carved ribs above the splayed and carved footrim; decorated in underglaze iron-black, the shoulder with a collar of radial petal-like brush-strokes, the body with a vegetal scroll between 3 decorative circular bands above, and 4 below; covered in a translucent, finely-crackled glaze, with some milky-blue flushes; the carved foot unglazed, and with a grey biscuit having a pinkish cast, Ht 12 cm.

Mr. K. T. Goh

Cf. no. 179.

181 Bottle

With cup-shaped mouth, sloping shoulder, and low-slung belly; the body with 6 vertical panels between two rows of decorative circular bands, in iron-black, the panels alternately displaying a double vegetal spiral scroll and a long filamentous undulating form like feathery grass (for which cf. no. 34); covered in a transparent greenish celadon glaze with a pronounced white crackle; the carved foot with an iron-red biscuit,

Ht 12.4 cm.

The University of Singapore

Its glaze and crackle relates no. 181 to nos. 172, 173, etc.

182　Kendi

With cup-shaped mouth; modelled in the shape of a male Mandarin duck. The features partly moulded, and partly described in underglaze iron-black; covered with a transparent crackled celadon glaze having a greenish cast like bottle-glass; the carved foot with a light-grey biscuit, having an orange cast, and with a prominent pontil-mark,

Ht 11.3 cm.

Mr. K. T. Goh

The basic form is close to no. 181. A somewhat similar kendi is illustrated in *Spinks II*, fig. 33, below (Phya Buranasiri Bongsa).

183　Kendi

Of flattened globular shape and with a mammiform spout; the neck with a flange below the mouthrim; decorated in underglaze iron-black; the neck-flange and the shoulder at the base of the neck with rosettes of lotus petals; the body with 6 complete and two interrupted ovoid panels containing vegetal sprays; the spout with 6 plantain leaves on the 'breast', and a rosette of lotus petals around the 'nipple'; with two incised circular bands on the lower body; the carved footrim with its outer side moulded and splayed, its inner side chamfered down to the base, disclosing an oatmeal biscuit and a distinct pontil scar,

Ht 13.9 cm.

The University of Singapore

184　Kendi

With flanged neck and mammiform spout; the body elaborately decorated in underglaze iron-black on a white slip, the scheme centred on three intertwined ogival medallions on the body, two containing peonies among vegetal sprays, and the third a bird; with a phoenix under the spout and a peony above; the body moulded with horizontal ribbing at the junctions of neck and foot; the unglazed lower body and the splayed foot with a terra-cotta biscuit; the base with traces of a pontil; the neck much repaired,

Ht 20.3 cm.

The Sinclair Collection

185　Kendi

With flanged neck and mammiform spout; decorated in underglaze iron-black on a grey body; the neck with a prominent flange below the mouthrim, bearing a lotus-leaf rosette; the sides of the neck and spout with upright plantain leaves; the upper shoulder with a collar of lotus petals; the lower shoulder with 7 decorative circular bands; the body with intertwined ogival medallions containing vegetal scrolls, each with a broad leaf; the outer side of the splayed footrim carved with several circular incisions, and with a chocolate-brown slip; the inner side of the footrim chamfered down to the base, both showing an oatmeal-coloured biscuit; the base with a pontil scar, the mouth repaired,

Ht 14.9 cm.

Mr. K. T. Goh

Once again the vegetal scroll with "broad leaf" relates the vessel to no. 151 (Sukhothai), 173, 175, 179, etc.

186　Bottle

Of flattened globular shape with a tall tubular neck, similar to no. 78; decorated in underglaze iron-black, the neck being divided into 3 zones by circular decorative bands, the upper with 3 panels enclosing leaf-forms, the middle with 4 diamond-shaped panels enclosing alternating geometrical and leaf-forms, and the lower with horizontally disposed leaf-sprays; the body with 4 roughly-drawn chrysanthemum rosettes alternating with vertical leaf-sprays; with two circular mouldings on the lower body; the carved and splayed footrim with a circular band of iron-brown slip on its outer side; the foot unglazed, with a putty-coloured biscuit and a pontil scar,

Ht 20.6 cm.

The Sinclair Collection

187 Covered potiche

With a high shoulder and 4 ring-handles; the outer side of the high foot deeply recessed above and moulded below; the lid with a plain knop handle; decorated in underglaze iron-black, the body with two registers, each of 8 rectangular panels filled alternately with cross-hatching and vegetal sprays; the moulded lid with 2 concentric decorative rings, the outer featuring the *prasat* motive (cf. no. 178) the inner with the motive seen on the upper cavetto of nos. 174, 175 and 178, here resembling debased Sanscrit characters; the carved foot and base with a bright rose-pink biscuit, of much lighter tone inside the distinct pontil scar,

Ht (with lid) 17.7 cm.

Professor and Mrs. K. J. Ratnam

188 Covered potiche

Of globular shape and with 4 ring-handles; the lid with a plain knop handle; decorated in underglaze iron-black, the lid with a rosette of 6 *prasats* (for which cf. 178 and 187), the shoulder and body each with 6 corresponding rectangular panels containing alternating vegetal sprays and 'fir-trees'; covered in a transparent, greenish celadon glaze with a fine white crackle; the splayed foot and base with a putty-coloured biscuit, lighter in tone inside the distinct pontil scar,

Ht (with lid) 13.6 cm.

Mr. William Willetts

Exhibiting several early features such as 'fir-trees' and white-veined crackle.

189 Covered potiche

With high shoulder and 4 ring-handles; the outer side of the footrim moulded, the lid with a plain knop handle; decorated in underglaze iron-black, much oxidised, and 'burnt' through the thin glaze; the body with 6 vertical panels, 3 with cross-hatching alternating with 3 with vegetal scrolls; the carved foot and base with a dark brick-red biscuit, and traces of a pontil,

Ht (with lid) 13.6 cm.

The University of Singapore

190 Covered potiche

Of flattened globular form; with two circular mouldings on the lower body; the splayed foot also moulded; the lid and body each with 6 prominent raised moulded vertical ribs; the panels between the ribs occupied by alternating summary vegetal forms and filamentous sprays painted in underglaze iron-black; the outer side of the footrim covered in a chocolate slip, as also the moulded vertical ribs and the plain knop handle; the carved foot and base with a beige-coloured biscuit,

Ht (with lid) 9.5 cm.

The University of Malaya

191 Covered potiche

Of tall ovoid form and with a moulded lid; the body decorated in underglaze iron-black; the shoulder with a circle of *prasats*, the body with 6 rectangular panels containing alternating cross-hatching and a vegetal motive organized about a diagonal cross; the tall carved footrim and base with a putty-coloured biscuit, pink at the edges,

Ht 10.1 cm.

The University of Singapore

192 Saucer-dish

With flattened mouthrim, and a raised and carved footrim; with iron-black underglaze decoration; the inside wall having 17 rows of three short lines arranged in a circle suggestive of the *pa kua* motive, and the centre medallion with a *chakra* or 'solar whorl'; the outside wall with six panels containing various figured motives; the foot unglazed, and with a grey biscuit; with a conspicuous oxidised iron-drop on the cavetto,

D. 13.6 cm.

Mr. William Willetts

193 Covered box

With moulded lid and plain knop (or lotus bud) handle; decorated in underglaze iron-black, the lid with an inner roughly drawn rosette, and an outer border of petal-like brush strokes (cf. no. 180); the body with a flat vegetal scroll between a pair of decorative circular bands above, and three below; the lower body with two circular mouldings above the carved foot; the foot and base unglazed, with an oatmeal-coloured biscuit, and distinct pontil scar,

Ht (with lid) 8.7 cm, d. 9.8 cm.

The University of Singapore

Cf. *Spinks II,* fig. 20, below (Frasché).

194 Covered box

With moulded lid and plain knop handle; decorated in underglaze iron-black, the lid and body with 8 corresponding rectangular panels, alternately containing cross-hatching and vegetal sprays; the lower body and carved foot unglazed, and with a grey biscuit here and there flushed pink,

Ht (with lid) 15.4 cm., d. 15.4 cm.

The University of Singapore

195 Covered box

With moulded lid and handle in the form of a fruit stalk; decorated in underglaze iron-black with 6 corresponding rectangular panels on body and lid alternately containing cross-hatching and vegetal sprays, and bordered by neatly drawn groups of parallel horizontal circular bands; the lower body with two circular mouldings, and it and the foot identical in form to that of no. 193; the foot and base un-

glazed, with a putty-coloured biscuit, and a distinct pontil-scar,

Ht (with lid) 7.9 cm., d. 11.4 cm.

The University of Singapore

196 Covered box

With moulded lid, and a handle in the form of a fruit stalk covered with a chocolate brown slip; decorated in underglaze iron-black, the lid and body with 6 corresponding rectangular panels, of which 3 contain cross-hatching and 3 vegetal sprays, bordered above and below by circular decorative bands; the lower body and foot identical in form to nos. 193 and 195; the foot and base unglazed, and with a greyish-pink biscuit,

Ht (with lid) 7.1 cm., d. 10.5 cm.

The University of Singapore

The lid-handle of this, and no. 195, is of the type called *obi himo* or 'sash cord' by the Japanese.

197 Covered box

With moulded lid, and a knop handle of double-gourd shape; decorated in underglaze iron-black with a series of broad circular decorative bands around the handle, and with 6 rectangular panels shared between body and lid, 3 with a vegetal spiral, 3 with cross-hatching; the splayed and carved foot continuous with the lower body and with a chocolate wash on its outer side, the inner side and base with a buff-coloured biscuit and distinct pontil scar,

Ht (with lid) 11.4 cm., d. 12.1 cm.

The University of Singapore

198 Covered box

With moulded lid, but without handle; decorated in underglaze iron-black with 6 corresponding rectangular panels on lid and body, 3 containing spiral vegetal scrolls and 3 with a concave element having vertical teeth like a comb, this element being repeated twice in the lid panels, three times in the body panels; the top of the lid with a radial pattern involving 16 spokes; the lower body with two circular mouldings; the body continuous with the outer side of the footrim, both being unglazed, and with a light-grey biscuit,

Ht (with lid) 7.5 cm., d. 10.4 cm.

Professor and Mrs. K. J. Ratnam

199 Covered box

With moulded lid and plain knop handle; decorated in underglaze iron-black with 6 corresponding rectangular panels on lid and body, 3 containing summary vegetal sprays, 3 with cross-hatching; bordered above, below, and between with groups of circular decorative bands; covered in a glassy, greenish, crackled glaze which has smudged the iron-black decoration of the lower body and run in irregular drops; the lower body and carved foot with a pale-grey biscuit flecked with iron-brown spots,

Ht (with lid) 10.1 cm., d. 10.8 cm.

Mr. William Willetts

200 Covered box

Of depressed globular form; the moulded lid with a plain knop handle; the lower body continuous with the outer side of the footrim, the latter covered with a brown wash; decorated in underglaze iron-black with circular decorative bands, between which are 6 rectangular panels shared between body and lid and containing alternating vegetal sprays and cross-hatching; the iron largely crystalline, and with the appearance of a patina; the lower body and carved foot unglazed, and with a brick-red biscuit,

Ht (with lid) 10.8 cm., d. 11.9 cm.

Mr. and Mrs. E. M. T. Lu

201 Covered box

With a moulded lid and plain knop handle; the flat lid surface bearing two attractively incised bisymmetrically-opposed vegetal scrolls covered in a brown slip; the sides of the lid and body decorated in underglaze iron-black, the former with a band of pendent trifid or heart-shaped forms alternating with single brush strokes, the latter with a

continuous undulating vegetal scroll; covered in a milky-white crackled glaze; the lower body and outer side of the foot with 3 deep circular incisions, and coated with a brown slip; the carved foot with a putty-coloured biscuit and traces of a pontil,

Ht 12.1 cm., d. 14.1 cm.

Mr. and Mrs. E. M. T. Lu

202 Covered box

Of depressed globular form, and with a nipple-like handle; decorated in underglaze iron-black, the lid with a circular band of trefoil and double-trefoil forms vaguely resembling cloves, the body with a continuous stylized vegetal scroll some-what suggestive of the Chinese cloud-scroll; the carved foot and base with a fine light-grey biscuit and clearly defined pontil scar,

Ht (with cover) 7 cm., d. 9.8 cm.

Mr. and Mrs. E. M. T. Lu

203 Covered box

The lid, with a flat top and scarcely raised nipple-like handle, decorated in underglaze iron-black with 7 radial elements, each of 3 brush-strokes; the sides of the lid with a saw-tooth border; the body with a band of 10 elements, each of 6 brush-stokes, similar to the *prasat* motive of nos. 187, 188, and 191; with an incised circular band above the foot; the carved footrim and base with a light-grey biscuit and traces of a pontil,

Ht (with lid) 7.1 cm., d. 9.7 cm.

Mr. William Willetts

204 Covered box

With moulded lid and plain knop handle; decorated in underglaze iron-black; the lid and body with 8 shared gadrooned panels alternately filled with 7 super-imposed palmettes and a mesh pattern reminiscent of *fleur-de-lys* (cf. also no. 191); all covered in a transparent glaze with milky-white patches; the carved foot-rim with two circular incisions on its outer side, its under and inner sides with a rose-pink biscuit; the base with a distinct pontil scar within which the biscuit is grey,

Ht (with lid) 15.6 cm., d. 15.6 cm.

Mrs. Helen Ling

205 Covered box

Of flattened form, with moulded lid, and handle in the form of a mangosteen fruit-stalk with 4 sepals; decorated in underglaze iron-black with a lotus-petal rosette surrounding the fruit-stalk; the sides of the lid and body each with 14 lotus panels enclosing alternating vegetal sprays and cross-hatched *fleur-de-lys* (for which cf. nos. 191, 204); the lower body with three circular carved incisions; the carved footrim glazed, and the base with a pink biscuit having a greyish tinge inside the pontil scar,

Ht (with lid) 15.6 cm., d. 19.5 cm.

The Sinclair Collection

206 Covered box

With no handle; decorated in underglaze black with a band of fish-scale ornament continuous over lid and body; the top of the lid with 12 circular decorative bands of varying thickness, the lower body with 7 similar; lacking a footrim; the lower body and base unglazed and with a firm pinkish-white biscuit in which iron-brown particles are liberally scattered; with a distinct pontil scar,

Ht (with lid) 9.5 cm., d. 12.6 cm.

The University of Singapore

The total absence of a footrim is exceptional; for an illustration of this foot see p. 192, upper right.

207 Covered box

With moulded lid and body and plain knop-handle; the flat lid-top and handle with a dark-chocolate slip; the lid with 12, the body with 13 moulded panels comprising alternating vegetal sprays and plantain leaves, pendent on the lid, upright on the body; the lower body sharply recessed inwards, and with a carved moulding between it and the foot; the

outer side of the footrim vertical, the inner chamfered down to the base; the lower body and foot unglazed, with a grey biscuit and distinct pontil scar,

Ht (with lid) 11.4 cm., d. 12.8 cm.

Mr. and Mrs. E. M. T. Lu

Cf. *Spinks II*, fig. 23, below (Phya Buranasiri Bongsa).

208 Covered box

With moulded lid and plain knop-handle; the handle and surrounding moulded collar with a dark-chocolate slip; the rims of the cover and body forming a flange; the lower body sharply recessed inwards, and with two circular incised mouldings above the foot; the lid-top decorated in underglaze iron black with a rosette of triangles filled with diagonal lines, the side of the lid with a band of inverted *prasats*; the body with a band of triangles like those on the lid; the lower body, carved footrim and base unglazed, and with an off-white biscuit,

Ht (with lid) 9.2 cm., d. 10.3 cm.

The University of Singapore

209 Covered box

The body and lid with 6 vertical sides; the turning-points of shoulder and lower body each with 6 lozenges drawn and moulded between the sides; the lid knop in the form of a bird with turned head; the bird enclosed in a moulded collar with a lotus petal rosette; the lid shoulder with 6 hexagonal figures containing alternating cross-hatched grounds and double vegetal spirals; the body with 6 octagons containing alternating cross-hatched ground patterns and cornucopias shedding vegetal sprays; the lower body with 6 half-hexagons repeating the design on the shoulder; the carved foot splayed outwards, and with a yellowish biscuit;

Ht (with lid) 10.6 cm., d. 11.1 cm.

The Sinclair Collection

A dreadful pot, but with many points of interest. Cf. *Spinks II*, fig. 26, below (Ladejinsky). Cf. also *Ram*, pl. 44.

210 Covered box

Of tall ovoid shape; decorated in underglaze black in the same schema as no. 209, the figures filled with alternating vegetal scrolls and *fleur-de-lys* forms (cf. nos. 191, 204, 205); the lid knop elaborately moulded in the form of a turtle, and covered in an irregular olivegreen celadon glaze; the lower body with one circular incised moulding above the foot; the outer side of the footrim splayed; the lower body and foot unglazed, with a somewhat gritty buff-coloured biscuit, and a distinct pontil mark,

Ht (with lid) 16 cm., d. 14.9 cm.

The Sinclair Collection

The inside box with a patchy light olivegreen celadon glaze, and the inside lid with an extraordinary cylindrical cavity, precisely cut, leading into the interior of the turtle.

211 Covered box

With moulded lid and plain knop handle; decorated in underglaze iron-black with 4 heart-shaped petals containing a scale pattern, points upward, continuous over body and lid, with vegetal sprays between; the lower body with one circular incised moulding above the splayed footrim; the foot with a pinkish-grey biscuit and a clear pontil mark,

Ht (with lid) 13.5 cm., d. 15.4 cm.

Mr. G. S. Cook

The inside of the box is glazed.

212 Covered box

In the form of a flower with 5 petals and 5 intercalated sepals; the 5 sepals (on the lid) moulded and raised; the lid with a plain knop-handle; decorated in underglaze iron-black with the above-mentioned flower in outline, the petals being filled with forms perhaps based on the cornucopia motive of no. 209; the foot without a footrim, but neatly chamfered down to a recessed flat base; the biscuit of a brownish-grey colour and somewhat

gritty, more definitely grey within the prominent pontil scar,

Ht (with lid) 10.1 cm., d. 13.1 cm.

Dr. D. Stephens

A somewhat similar form is of course known in Annamese blue-and-white: cf. *Okuda*, fig. 48 and *Locsin*, fig. 155, foreground. The recessed base is exceptional. An illustration of the foot appears on p. 192, lower left.

213 Kendi

Modelled in the shape of a personage seated on a sacred goose *(hamsa)* his hands in *anjali*: the head of the personage is also the stopper that closes the mouth of the vessel, the goose's mouth being its spout; the modelled anatomical parts picked out in a dark greenish-brown pigment on a light-grey slipped ground; the glaze largely eroded; the unglazed base and inner side of footrim with a reddishgrey biscuit,

Ht 29.2 cm.

The Sinclair Collection

A similar figure is illustrated in *Spinks II*, fig. 34 (de Aya), from the Philippines.

214 Building ornament

In the form of a lion guardian, *simha*, and meant to be used as a roof endtile; the anatomical features partly modelled and partly picked out in underglaze iron-black,

Ht 50.8 cm.

The Sinclair Collection

From Bali. Compare a closely similar specimen in *Spinks I*, fig. 1 (Djakarta Museum), from south Sulawesi; such ceramic figures are generally attributed to Sukhothai, as does Spinks, but according to *Griswold I*, p. 22, they were much more probably made at the Ba Yang kiln about 1 km. north of the north wall of Sri Satchanalai (old Sawankoloke).

215 Head

Fragment: the anatomical features and head-dress modelled in relief, the details emphasised in iron-black pigment; covered with a grey-blue glaze mottled in brown,

Ht 10.8 cm.

The University of Malaya

216 Head of a *yaksha*

Fragment; the features modelled, the eyes and eyebrows emphasised with iron-black pigment; covered in a milky-blue glaze on a brownish-grey biscuit,

Ht 15.9 cm.

The University of Malaya

Cf. *Indicna*, fig. 71 (National Museum, Bangkok); cf. also *Ram*, pl. 36.

217 Sherd

Consisting of most of the centre medallion of a large dish; the design, of a fish among waterweeds, drawn in iron-black on a cream biscuit; the footrim roughly carved, and with a brownish-grey coarse biscuit; the base with a biscuit somewhat lighter in colour, and with traces of a pontil measuring no less than 9.5 cm. in diameter,

Max. d. 12.7 cm.

The University of Malaya

Of the Sawankoloke rendering of the fish motive Spinks says that it is more delicately drawn than its Sukhothai neighbour, and is combined with a floral or water-weed background; and, moreover, that it is "a rather sluggish almost sleepy looking fellow" compared with that of Sukhothai which is "lively [and] rollicking". For another comparison between the two renderings cf. *Ram*, pl. 32a (Sukhothai) and 32b (Sawankoloke).

GROUP FOUR: SAWANKOLOKE WARES

Family 2. Brown-glazed monochromes.

218 Bottle

Of globular shape, the shoulder sloping obliquely; with 2 ring-handles joining the shoulder to the cup-like mouth; the shoulder with 12 circular gouged decorative bands; covered in a mottled dark-brown glaze; the lower body and carved foot with

a dark red-brown biscuit; the base with a distinct pontil scar,

Ht 15.7 cm.

The University of Singapore

For a closely similar piece cf. *Spinks I,* fig. 14, right (Djakarta), from Tapanuli, Sumatra.

219 Bottle

Similar to no. 218 but rounder and with a higher shoulder; the shoulder with 10 circular gouged decorative bands; the inner side of the carved footrim shallower than in no. 203,

Ht 17.5 cm.

The University of Singapore

220 Bottle

Smaller than nos. 218 and 219, but taller in proportion; with 6 circular gouged decorative bands on the shoulder; in respect of glaze, biscuit, and potting technique identical with nos. 218 and 219,

Ht 14.6 cm.

The University of Singapore

Cf. *Spinks I,* fig. 50, right (Djakarta), from Benkoelen.

221 Bottle

Similar to no. 220, but somewhat smaller in build, and more precisely potted; with 10 circular gouged decorative bands on the shoulder; the footrim neatly carved, the inner side shallow, as in no. 219; the base with a distinct pontil scar,

Ht 14.3 cm.

The University of Singapore

Cf. *Spinks I,* fig. 17 (Djakarta), from Sumatra.

222 Bottle

Smaller than nos. 220 and 221, yet taller in proportion; with 9 circular incised decorative bands on the shoulder; covered in a caramel-coloured glaze that has thinned above and formed tear-drops below; the lower body and carved foot unglazed, and with a buff-coloured biscuit,

Ht 13.2 cm.

The University of Singapore

223 Bottle

Similar in shape to 222 but smaller; the shoulder with 7 circular incised decorative bands and the upper body with 26 vertical decorative incised lines; coated with a dark chocolate-brown glaze that has thinned above and run in tear-drops below; the lower body and carved foot unglazed and with a light brownish-pink biscuit,

Ht 10.8 cm.

Dr. and Mrs. K. H. Lim

224 Chicken figurine

With moulded anatomical parts; covered in a dark caramel glaze, the lower body and plain foot unglazed and with a pinkish-grey biscuit,

Ht 5.5 cm.

Mrs. Helen Ling

For a similar figurine cf. *Spinks II*, fig. 37, middle right (Ladejinsky).

225 Elephant figurine

The body covered with a dull caramel glaze; the legs unglazed and with an ochre biscuit; the elephant carrying a large bowl on its back,

Ht 7.6 cm.

Mrs. Helen Ling

For a similar figurine cf. *Spinks II*, fig. 42, above (Ladejinsky). Cf. also no. 236.

226 Elephant figurine

Similar to no. 225, but instead of the bowl the elephant carries a mahout, his hands in *anjali*,

Ht 9.5 cm.

Mrs. Helen Ling

227 Flask *(hu lu p'ing)*

Gourd-shaped, and of miniature size, with everted mouthrim and two ring-handles on the shoulder; with a deep caramel-coloured glaze on the upper body; the lower body and carved foot with a buff-coloured biscuit,

Ht 6 cm.

Mr. J. M. van Baak

For one similar cf. *Spinks II*, fig. 5, above right (Frasché).

228 Covered box

The lid with a handle in the form of a fruit-stalk surrounded by a collar similar to that of no. 208; the lid and body covered in a matt and mottled caramel-coloured glaze; the lower body with 2 gouged incised rings above the carved footrim; the base with a buff biscuit and traces of a pontil,

D. 10.5 cm.

Professor and Mrs. K. J. Ratnam

229 Covered box

The lid moulded, and with a plain knop handle; covered in a thin light-brown glaze, much abraded; the lower body with a single gouged incised ring above the recessed carved footrim; the foot with a faint orange-pink biscuit and traces of a pontil,

D. 10.1 cm.

Mr. S. R. Parker

The glaze has decayed in a curious way, the upper light-brown layer exposing a light-grey layer underneath; this is perhaps unoxydized glaze, not a slip.

230 Covered potiche

With a high shoulder and 3 ring-handles; the domed lid having a plain knop handle; the shoulder with 4 gouged circular decorative bands; covered in a mottled chestnut-brown glaze; the lower body, carved splayed footrim and base unglazed and with a brick-red biscuit, grey inside the pontil scar,

Ht (with lid) 10.1 cm.

The University of Singapore

231 Potiche

Of tall ovoid shape, with three ring-handles on the high shoulder; lacking lid; the upper shoulder with 2 gouged circular decorative bands, the lower shoulder with 8 similar; the body with a belt of gouged vertical striations, and the lower body with 6 gouged circular decorative bands; covered in a rich caramel-coloured glaze which has run in tear-drops onto parts of the lower body; the lower body, carved splayed footrim, and base with a dense dark brick-red biscuit, grey within the pontil mark,

Ht 15.6 cm.

Mr. William Willetts

232 Covered potiche

Of an urn shape; the domed lid with a plain knop handle; the shoulder with 3 ring-handles as in no. 231; covered in an uneven chocolate glaze which, where eroded, has left a tan-coloured surface beneath; the lower body and carved foot unglazed, and with a vermillion biscuit,

Ht (with lid) 18.6 cm.

The Sinclair Collection

233 *Kendi* or water dropper

In the form of a squatting figure with humped back, carrying in the right hand a small bag (? or fly whisk) and upholding in the left a jar whose opening is also that of the *kendi* itself; the back and sides of the body incised with patterns of cross-hatching; the upper part of the body covered with a mottled olive-brown glaze, the lower biscuited grey with an orange cast,

Ht 10.3 cm.

Mr. K. T. Goh

Cf. also no. 262. Similar *kendis* are illustrated in *Spinks I*, fig. 26, right middle and right (Djakarta), and fig. 27, middle (Djakarta). The significance of these and other Thai ceramic figurines is discussed in *Spinks II*, pp. 80-88.

234 Mahamaya or Mahalakshmi

Ceramic figurine probably representing the Goddess Lakshmi receiving a lustration from two rearing elephants; the figures covered with a mottled caramel-coloured glaze, the hollow sockle with a pinkish-brown biscuit,

Ht 17.5 cm.

The University of Singapore

235 Figurine

In the form of a lion or lion-dog; covered in a mottled olive-brown glaze,

Ht 8 cm.

The University of Singapore

236 Ceramic sculpture

In the form of a caparisoned ceremonial war elephant, with 2 mahouts, a 'dragon jar' in the place of honour, and 8 attendants placed two against each leg; the anatomical parts modelled and defined by incised lines, partly covered with a mottled caramel-coloured glaze and partly in biscuit, the latter light grey in colour,

Ht 32.7 cm., l. 36.8 cm.

The University of Singapore

From Bandjar Masin, Kalimantan. Several similar elephants are known, as for example *Spinks I*, fig. 20. (Djakarta), from southeast Kalimantan, *Spinks II*, fig. 41 (H.R.H. Prince Bhanubhandu Yugala), and *Bangkok*, pl. 37 (Nai Prapot Paorohit), as well as others in local Singapore collections. On several of these elephants a curious rosette is to be seen on the head, between the eyes and the ears, and comprising a small hole or pin-prick in the paste surrounded by 6 others of the same size. No. 221 has a similar rosette, but larger, and incised not pierced, on both sides of the head between the ear flap and the base of the tusk. According to Spinks, the rosette symbolised the Buddhist wheel of the Law, *dharma-cakra*, and the elephant served as a reliquary, the holy relic (*phrya dhatu*) being consigned to the receptacle on the animal's head. Cf. *Spinks II*, pp. 82-4.

GROUP FOUR: SAWANKOLOKE WARES

Family 3. Pearly-white glazed monochromes.

237 Vase

Of bottle gourd shape, and with 2 ring-handles at the junction of the two elements; covered with a smooth, matt, pearly-white glaze; the lower body and carved foot unglazed, and with a light-grey biscuit,

Ht 20.5 cm.

The Sinclair Collection

For a similar form, though smaller and with a celadon glaze, cf. *Spinks I*, fig. 47, left (Djakarta), from central Sulawesi.

238 Covered potiche

Of an elegant shape like an urn; the domed lid with a plain knop handle; the body decorated with vertical oblique gouged striations enclosed above by a single horizontal gouged decorative band, and below by 3 similar bands; the outer side of the carved footrim slightly recessed; the foot with an off-white biscuit,

Ht (with lid) 14.8 cm.

Dr. D. Stevens

239 Covered box

The flat upper surface of the lid with a circular register of cross-hatching, and the nipple-like depressed knop handle with a collar of star-points (with which compare nos. 208 and 228), all covered in a chocolate slip; the sides of the lid and the box with a pearly-white opaque glaze; the inside of the box with a thin translucent green-tinted glaze; the lower body with 2 circular incised mouldings above the foot; the carved footrim and base with a pinkish-white biscuit and traces of a pontil,

D. 9.7 cm.

Mr. and Mrs. E. M. T. Lu

240 Covered box

With a persimmon (*kakinote*) calyx painted in a dark olive-brown coloured slip; the sides of the lid and box covered with a pearly-white glaze; the inside of the box with a thin translucent greenish glaze; the lower body with two circular incised mouldings above the foot; the lower body, carved footrim, and base, with a fine dense biscuit containing iron brown particles and flushed a delicate salmon-pink, grey within the clearly-defined pontil scar,

D. 9.2 cm.

Mr. S. R. Parker

An illustration of the foot is shown on p. 192, lower right.

241 Bowl

Of lotus-pod (*lien tzǔ*) shape; covered inside and out with a pearly-white glaze, crackled on the outside wall; the lower body, carved footrim, and base with a brownish-red biscuit and pontil trace,

D. 14.3 cm.

Dr. D. Stevens

A similar bowl is illustrated in *Spinks I*, fig. 5, right (Djakarta), from Kediri, East Java.

242 Potiche

Large, and of ovoid shape, lacking a lid; covered with a matt, crackled, pearly-white glaze on the outside wall, and with traces of a pitted glaze within; the carved footrim and base with a pinkish-grey biscuit, beige within the distinct pontil mark,

Ht 16 cm.

The Sinclair Collection

For a similar potiche (with lid) cf. *Spinks II*, fig. 10, above (Ladejinsky).

243 Covered potiche

Of depressed globular shape and with 3 ring-handles on the shoulder, above which are 3 circular incised bands; with a domed lid having a plain knop handle; covered with an opalescent pearly-white glaze that has run in gummy tear-drops onto the lower body; the latter, and the splayed carved footrim and base, with a dark brick-red biscuit, grey within the pontil scar,

Ht (with lid) 11.4 cm.

The University of Singapore

For a similar potiche, which also has the incised bands, cf. *Spinks II*, fig. 10, below (Ladejinsky); cf. also *Locsin*, pl. 187, from Calatagan.

244 Covered potiche

With a squashed globular form, and 2 incised circular bands below the mouthrim; the domed lid with a plain knop handle; covered in a pearly bluish-white glaze with a minute white-veined crackle; the lower body with 2 circular bands above the plain foot; with a beige-coloured biscuit and a distinct pontil trace,

Ht (with lid) 9.5 cm.

Mr. and Mrs. Trevor Rutter

For a similar foot *sans* footrim cf. no. 206.

245 Covered potiche

With 3 ring-handles mounted on the shoulder, above which is a circular incised band; the domed lid with a plain knop handle; covered in a lustrous pearly-white glaze; the lower body, carved footrim, and base with a chalky pinkish-white biscuit,

Ht (with lid) 11.6 cm.

Mr. and Mrs. Trevor Rutter

246 Covered potiche

Similar in shape to nos. 243, 244 and 245; with 3 ring-handles mounted on the shoulder, above which are 2 circular incised mouldings; the domed lid with a plain knop handle; covered in a degraded but smooth and matt pearly-white glaze; the lower body, carved footrim, and base with an oatmeal-coloured biscuit, flushed with pink outside the pontil scar,

Ht 14.4 cm.

The University of Singapore

247 Covered potiche

Of flattened globular form, with a keel-shaped shoulder; the domed lid with a plain knop handle; the body with a register of deeply-gouged vertical flutings closed below by 3 circular incised bands; covered with a polished, pearly-white glaze; the inside of the box with a translucent greenish glaze; the footrim neatly carved, its outer side slightly recessed; the lower body and foot with a bright terracotta biscuit, grey inside the pontil scar,

Ht (with lid) 13.5 cm.

The Sinclair Collection

248 Bottle

Of *yü hu ch'un p'ing* shape and with a delicate cup-shaped mouth, below which

are two moulded and pigmented decorative bands; covered in a matt, pearly-white glaze, somewhat degraded; the lower body and carved foot with a putty-coloured biscuit speckled with black, lighter in tone within the pontil mark,

Ht 25.5 cm.

The Sinclair Collection

For a similar form in the biscuited and celadon groups see nos. 259 and 300; for a brown-glazed monochrome example cf. *Spinks I,* fig. 50 (Djakarta), from Acheh, north Sumatra.

GROUP FOUR: SAWANKOLOKE WARES

Family 4. Incised biscuited wares.

249 Covered box

Of *kakinote* (persimmon) type with 12 sepals; the sides of the lid and body each ornamented with a vine-trail incised on an oatmeal biscuit and filled with a chocolate-coloured slip; the lower body with 2 circular mouldings coated with a brown slip above the foot; the carved footrim and shallow base unglazed, and with an oatmeal biscuit, somewhat greyer inside the pontil scar,

D. 12.4 cm.

The University of Singapore

250 Covered box

Of *kakinote* (persimmon) type with 9 sepals; the lid with a saw-tooth border filled with a caramel slip; the body with an incised vine-scroll illuminated with a degraded white glaze over a warm buff-coloured biscuit, the background roughly filled in with a caramel-coloured glaze; the lower body with 2 circular mouldings above the carved footrim; the foot with a grey biscuit, flushed pink outside the pontil scar,

D. 10.6 cm.

Mr. and Mrs. Frank Lammers

251 Covered box

Of *kakinote* (persimmon) type with 11 sepals; the décor, and its organisation, similar to that of no. 250; the vine-scroll illuminated in a pearly-white degraded glaze; the lower body with 2 circular mouldings above the carved footrim; the foot unglazed, with a grey biscuit and pontil scar,

D. 12 cm.

The University of Singapore

252 Covered box

Of *kakinote* (persimmon) type with 9 sepals; the décor similar to that of nos. 250 and 251, but the vine-trail on the body finer, and filled with a dark-brown slip on a background of oatmeal biscuit partially covered with a degraded white glaze; (cf. no. 249); the lower body moulded above the carved footrim; the foot unglazed, with a pontil scar and grey biscuit,

D. 9.6 cm.

The University of Singapore

253 Covered box

Of *kakinote* (persimmon) type with 8 sepals; the décor of the type of nos. 250 and 251; the vine-trail illuminated with a white glaze, the background with a chestnut-coloured slip; the lower body with 2 circular mouldings above the carved footrim; the foot unglazed and with a pink biscuit, grey inside the pontil mark,

D. 9 cm.

Mr. William Willetts

254 Covered box

With a flat lid; the nipple-like knop standing on a small raised circular platform, surrounded by an incised calyx or floral medallion reserved in a degraded white glaze on a chocolate-brown ground; the sides of the lid and body with a décor similar to that of nos. 250, 251 and 253; the body with 2 circular mouldings above the carved footrim; the unglazed foot with a grey biscuit,

D. 9.5 cm.

The University of Singapore

255 Miniature covered box

Of *kakinote* type and with 10 sepals; the décor organised in the manner of nos. 250, 251, 253 and 254, the saw-teeth and vine-trail illuminated with a degraded white glaze; the lower body with 2 circular mouldings above the carved footrim; the foot unglazed and with a pinkish-grey biscuit,

D. 6 cm.

Mr. S. R. Parker

256 Covered box

Of *kakinote* type, with 10 sepals on the calyx inside which is a 7-point star; with a rosette of 19 petals outside the calyx; the sides of the lid and body with a minutely incised floral trail illuminated in brown slip reserved on a white-glazed background; the lower body with 2 circular mouldings above the carved footrim; the foot unglazed, with a grey biscuit and pontil scar,

D. 10.1 cm.

The University of Singapore

257 Covered box

With an elaborately moulded lid; the plain knop-handle surrounded by 2 circular registers, the inner with an incised rosette of petal-like forms, the outer with a plant-scroll; the side of the lid with a saw-tooth pattern; the body with a finely-detailed plant-scroll and 2 circular mouldings above the carved foot; all covered with a thin caramel-coloured slip, which appears darker in the incisions; the foot unglazed and with a pinkish-grey biscuit, but grey inside the pontil scar,

D. 13.5 cm.

The University of Singapore

258 Jar

With a high shoulder like a potiche, but lacking a mouthrim or cover; with an incised design of 4 paired vine leaves on the shoulder, a vine-scroll on the body, and a saw-tooth register on the lower body; with a circular moulding above the carved footrim; the foot unglazed, with a putty-coloured biscuit and a pontil scar,

Ht 9 cm.

Mr. and Mrs. Frank Lammers

For a similar jar, but having 4 ring-handles cf. *Spinks I,* fig. 40, right (Djakarta), from Djambi, Sumatra.

259 Ewer

Of *yü hu ch'un p'ing* shape, but laterally flattened and moulded into an 8-sided form in which the two lateral panels predominate; the neck very narrow, and the mouth cup-shaped; the handle and spout elaborately moulded, the handle to represent a dragon, the spout a long-necked creature emerging from the open mouth of a monster; the body finely incised on the one side with a scrolling vine, on the other with a *ch'i-lin* rampant on a scrolled ground; the incisions partly picked out, and the vessel partly covered, in a rich brown slip on a beige biscuit; the carved foot unglazed, and with a pinkish-white biscuit,

Ht 25.4 cm.

The Sinclair Collection

The device of a long-necked crested bird emerging from the jaws of a *makara* (crocodile-dragon) is repeated over and over again in bas-relief at the sides of carved Buddha images in the 5th-century A.D. Buddhist caves at Nasik and Ajanta in Western India; it bears a striking resemblance to that of no. 259. But in the case of no. 259 the motive probably represents a *naga* (snake god) emerging from the jaws of another, a perennial subject of Thai art. Cf. *Ram,* pl. 41, for a Sukhothai example in the form of a building ornament.

260 Water-dropper

In the shape of a double Mandarin duck *(yüan yang),* the male with open throat; the features incised and painted with a caramel-coloured slip; the plain foot with a grey biscuit,

L. 11.3 cm.

Mrs. Helen Ling

261 Ornament

In the form of a puffer-fish (with a human face); the facial features, and the dorsal, caudal, pelvic and pectoral fins moulded, the pectoral fins doubling as ears; with scales indicated as incised parallel bands of joined scallops; these and the facial features picked out in a caramel-coloured slip; the body and flat foot unglazed, and with a dull pinkish-grey biscuit,

Ht 13.3 cm.

The Sinclair Collection

262 Kendi

Of similar form to no. 233, but the attributes reversed; the chest and humped back nude; the lower body clothed, and the clothing and snail-shell coiffure indicated by a chocolate-brown slip,

Ht 8.1 cm.

Mr. K. T. Goh

GROUP FOUR: SAWANKOLOKE WARES

Family 5. Celadons

263 Ring-handled bottle

Of squat globular shape; lightly incised with four floral rosettes in medallions on the shoulder; between the shoulder and body a group of 7 circular incised decorative bands; the body with gouged vertical striations; all covered in a highly variegated celadon glaze showing oxidation and reduction effects, as well as heavy runs of glaze down the striations, as it were resembling stalactites; the carved footrim and base unglazed, and with a bright terracotta biscuit and clear pontil scar,

Ht 17.8 cm.

The University of Singapore

Cf. of many published examples, *Spinks I,* fig. 37, left (Djakarta), from Bali, and *Spinks II,* fig. 6, above (Frasché).

264 Ring-handled bottle

Of squat globular shape; the shoulder decorated with a finely-incised design of ten lotus petals, with carved decorative circular bands above and below; the body with gouged vertical striations; the lower body and foot unglazed, with a bright terracotta biscuit, of a lighter brown inside the conspicuous pontil scar,

Ht 13.6 cm.

Mr. G. S. Cook

265 Ring-handled bottle

Of squat globular shape; the shoulder with a moulded ridge at the turning-point; the body with several circular carved decorative bands above a register of lightly-gouged vertical striations; covered in a duck-egg blue celadon glaze with pale-blue and creamy-white furnace transmutations, and having a dark-veined crackle; the lower body, carved footrim and base unglazed, and with a terracotta biscuit, of a lighter shade within the pontil scar,

Ht 14.7 cm.

The University of Singapore

266 Ring-handled bottle

Of squat globular shape; the shoulder with carved circular decorative bands above and below a summary floral border; the body with lightly gouged vertical striations; covered with a delicate crackled sea-green glaze; the lower body, outer side of footrim and base unglazed, and with a bright terracotta biscuit covered with a wood-ash glaze except within the prominent pontil scar; the under side of the footrim with a grey biscuit, and perhaps therefore ground down after firing,

Ht 16.2 cm.

Mr. S. R. Parker

267 Ring-handled bottle

Of globular shape; with 3 carved peony medallions on the shoulder between rows of carved circular decorative bands; the body with gouged vertical striations; covered in an olive-green celadon glaze transmuted to sea-green on the reduced side of the pot, and with a medium-sized crackle; the foot unglazed and with

a terracotta biscuit, of lighter shade within the pontil scar,

Ht 19.2 cm.

Mr. B. C. Lim

268 Ring-handled bottle

Of a squat globular shape; with some 15 incised circular decorative bands on the shoulder, and gouged vertical striations on the body; thinly covered with a dark olive-green celadon glaze; the lower body and carved foot unglazed, with a pale pinkish-beige biscuit and pontil scar,

Ht 14.3 cm.

Mr. Edwin Lee

269 Ring-handled bottle

Of squat globular shape, the upper shoulder with a finely-carved floral scroll between decorative circular bands above and below; the lower shoulder with a register of combed "comma" pattern separated from the body by 5 incised circular decorative bands; the body with gouged vertical striations; all covered in a clear grey-green celadon glaze with a fine crackle; the lower body and carved foot with a salmon-pink biscuit of a powdery appearance, and with a pontil scar,

Ht 17.1 cm.

Mr. and Mrs. Frank Hickley

270 Ring-handled bottle

Of globular shape with a long sloping shoulder; the shoulder with some 14 carved circular decorative bands; covered in a dark olive-green celadon glaze with a dark-veined crackle; the lower body and carved foot with a bright terracotta biscuit, lighter within the pontil mark, the under side of the footrim perhaps ground down,

Ht 15.4 cm.

Mr. and Mrs. Frank Lammers

271 Ring-handled bottle

Much similar to no. 270 but in addition with short gouged vertical striations on the body; covered in a dark olive-green celadon glaze with a dark-veined crackle; the outer side of the footrim splayed outwards; the lower body and foot with a dark terracotta biscuit, of lighter shade inside the pontil scar,

Ht 15 cm.

The University of Singapore

272 Ring-handled bottle

Similar to nos. 270 and 271 but taller in proportion; with 10 carved circular decorative bands on the somewhat square shoulder; covered in a dark olive-green celadon glaze with some furnace transmutations; the outer side of the carved footrim splayed outwards and again inwards; the lower body and foot unglazed, with a terracotta biscuit and distinct pontil scar,

Ht 16.8 cm.

The University of Singapore

273 Ring-handled bottle

Of globular shape and with a long sloping shoulder; the shoulder with a register of lotus leaves, summarily carved, between 5 carved circular decorative bands above and below; the body with a pattern of cross-hatching done with a 4-toothed comb; lightly covered in a pale olive-green celadon glaze worn through at the mouthrim and on the handles; the outer side of the footrim markedly splayed outwards and again inwards; the lower body and foot unglazed, with a yellowish-pink biscuit, less pink inside the pontil scar,

Ht 17.5 cm.

The University of Singapore

274 Ring-handled bottle

Of globular shape; the shoulder with strongly gouged vertical striations between 3 carved decorative circular bands above and below; the lower body reciprocally carved with strong gouged vertical striations; covered in a matt pale blue-green celadon glaze; the lower body and

crudely carved foot with a beige-coloured biscuit,

Ht 13.3 cm.

The University of Singapore

275 Ring-handled bottle

Of flattened globular shape; the upper shoulder with a neatly carved and well composed scroll comprising three peony blooms between three carved circular decorative bands above and two below; the body with gouged vertical striations, the upper ends incised so as to resemble lotus-leaf flutings; covered with a pale sea-green celadon glaze; the lower body and carved foot with a pink biscuit and clear pontil scar,

Ht 14.1 cm.

Mr. S. R. Parker

276 Ring-handled bottle

Of squat globular form, with moulded shoulder; the shoulder incised with three peony blossoms in medallions, the upper body with a pair of broken undulating combed bands; all covered in a pale sea-green celadon glaze; the under and inner sides of the footrim and the base unglazed, and with a deep pink biscuit, lighter in tone inside the pontil scar,

Ht 14.7 cm.

The Sinclair Collection

277 Ring-handled bottle

Of globular shape and with moulded shoulder; the latter carved with 3 peony blossoms in medallions between 4 carved circular decorative bands above and 3 below; the body with gouged vertical striations having an incised scalloped combed band over their upper ends (cf. no. 275); covered in a sea-green celadon glaze; the lower body and carved foot unglazed and with a pink biscuit, of a greyer tone within the pontil scar,

Ht 16.7 cm.

The University of Singapore

278 Ring-handled jar

Of similar form to no. 274, but miniature in size; the shoulder with strongly incised gouged striations, reciprocated on the lower body; covered in a thin glassy sea-green celadon glaze with a crackle, the body being visible beneath; the foot plain, with flat base, and with a beige-coloured biscuit,

Ht 6.6 cm.

Mr. William Willetts

279 Pair of figurines

In a seated embrace; the figures wear *panungs* decorated with an all-over pattern of large iron-black blobs; the facial features also picked out in iron-black; all covered in a grey-green celadon glaze; the flat foot separately moulded, and with a grey-brown biscuit,

Ht 9 cm.

The Sinclair Collection

Cf. *Spinks II*, fig. 38, lower (Ladejinsky), and p. 79.

280 Maternity figurine

The head replaced; the mother, with child, covered in a grey-green celadon glaze on a brownish-pink biscuit,

Ht 9.5 cm.

The University of Malaya

Cf. *Spinks II*, fig. 38, above (Ladejinsky). For a discussion of the significance of the human female decapitated figurines cf. *Spinks II*, pp. 86-8. The theory is that the pregnant woman, by breaking the head off one of these images would, by sympathetic magic, transfer to the image the dangers attendant on childbirth. No. 280 comes from the kiln-site.

281 Dog

The body covered in a grey-green celadon glaze, the legs and lower body unglazed, revealing a coarse pink biscuit with whitish granular inclusions,

L. 7.6 cm.

The University of Malaya

282 Dish

With a foliate rim, the flattened lip with a combed pattern following the contours of the foliations; the cavetto with 2 incised circular decorative bands above, beneath which is a combed undulating band, then 2 more incised circular bands, then a combed scalloped band; the centre medallion with two groups of 3 incised circular decorative bands; the outside wall with gouged vertical striations; all covered in a grey-green and glassy celadon glaze with a wide crackle; the carved foot with a salmon-pink biscuit and a wood-ash glaze, except within the pontil-mark where the biscuit is lighter in tone and unglazed; the upper part of the pontil still adhering to the base,

D. 23.5 cm.

The University of Malaya

A classic example of the effects of oxidation and reduction inside the base; for an illustration see p. 193, upper left.

283 Dish

With a foliate rim, the flattened lip with an incised band repeating the contours of the rim; the cavetto with a combed pattern comprising 4 large figures made up of several pairs of confronting comma-shaped elements, arranged like the layers of an onion; the centre medallion with a *cakra* surrounded by two groups of 4 incised circular decorative bands; the outside wall plain; all covered in a limpid blue-green celadon glaze worn thin over the carved foliated rim; the foot roughly carved, with an orange-pink biscuit and traces of a very large pontil.

D. 25.5 cm.

The University of Singapore

This cavetto motive was commonly employed on the larger Sawankoloke celadon dishes and bowls. For a similar dish (without a scalloped rim) cf. *Locsin*, fig. 164, above, right.

284 Bowl

With everted rim and flattened lip, the cavetto with an upper decorative band of combed broken comma-pattern enclosed above and below by 2 incised circular decorative bands; the centre medallion with a small summarily-incised spiral; the outside wall with gouged vertical striations; all covered in a grey-green glassy celadon glaze with a medium crackle; the carved foot and base with a terra-cotta biscuit, of lighter tone inside the pontil scar,

D. 28 cm.

The University of Singapore

285 Bowl

With everted rim and flattened lip; the upper cavetto with a continuous carved band of short curved lines in vertical columns of 3 or 4 between 2 pairs of incised circular decorative bands; the centre medallion with a small incised spiral; the outside wall with carelessly gouged curved vertical striations; all covered in an olive-green glaze with a reduced blue-green area on the outside wall; the carved foot with a brick-red biscuit, beige-coloured inside the pontil scar,

D. 28.1 cm.

The University of Singapore

286 Deep bowl

With everted rim; the inside lip with 5 incised circular decorative bands; the cavetto with 3 large 'onion-pattern' motives (for which cf. no. 283), closed below with 4 incised circular decorative bands; the centre medallion with a small incised circular band; the outer wall plain; all covered in a glassy grey-green celadon glaze having a fine white-veined crackle; the lower body and foot unglazed and with a pinkish-brown biscuit of powdery appearance, slightly less pink inside the pontil scar,

D. 24.1 cm.

Professor and Mrs. K. J. Ratnam

287 Potiche

Of deep bowl-shape; the mouthrim slightly everted, the bulbous body with 5 incised circular decorative bands above a main register of paired incised parallel lines

laid in a cross-hatched pattern and enclosed below by 5 incised circular decorative bands; the lower body with vertical incised striations laid in 2's and 3's; covered in a pale apple-green celadon glaze of varying hue; the roughly carved foot unglazed, with a pale-pink biscuit and traces of a pontil,

Ht 17.8 cm.

Mrs. Helen Ling

288 Deep bowl

With strongly everted mouthrim and a distinct neck; the body with 3 circular incised bands above a main zone comprising strongly gouged curved vertical striations, closed below by a spiral of 6 incised circular decorative bands; covered in a somewhat eroded grey-green glaze; the lower body and carved foot unglazed, and with a brick-red biscuit, beige-coloured inside the pontil scar,

D. 21.9 cm.

The Sinclair Collection

289 Bowl

With everted mouthrim; the upper cavetto decorated with a continuous combed wavy band set against an incised herring-bone ground, with 3 circular incised decorative bands above and below; the outer wall with gouged vertical striations; all covered with a sea-green and somewhat glassy crackled celadon glaze; the carved foot unglazed, with a powdery pink biscuit speckled with black, and with a pontil scar,

D. 20.8 cm.

Mr. K. T. Goh

290 Bowl

With everted rim and flattened lip; the upper cavetto with a continuous combed wavy band between rows of oblique cuts above and below and enclosed between 2 pairs of incised circular decorative bands; the centre medallion with 2 similar bands; the outer wall with gouged vertical striations; all covered in a sea-green crackled celadon glaze; the lower body and foot unglazed, with a rust-red biscuit and imperfect pontil scar,

D. 26.6 cm.

Dr. D. Stevens

For a similar décor see *Spinks I,* fig. 23 (Djakarta), from Pasuruhan, eastern Java.

291 Bowl

With everted mouthrim and flattened lip; the décor similar to that of no. 290 but minus the centre medallion; the outside wall with gouged lotus-leaf flutings; all covered in a fine grey-green celadon glaze; the carved foot unglazed and with a terracotta biscuit, grey within the pontil scar,

D. 27 cm.

The University of Singapore

For an illustration of the foot see p. 193, upper right.

292 Dish

With a 12-foil rim and flattened lip; the cavetto with a well-devised pattern of 3 neatly carved peony scrolls, the centre medallion with a lotus rosette; the outside wall plain; covered in a matt sea-green celadon glaze lying deep in the depressed floor of the dish; the carved foot with a grey biscuit inside the pontil mark, and outside with orange flushes,

D. 32.4 cm.

Dr. and Mrs. K. H. Lim

For a similar dish cf. *Locsin,* pl. 163, and for an even more closely similar piece, allegedly Ming, cf. *Locsin,* pl. 129.

293 Dish

With an everted rim and flattened lip; the cavetto with a circlet of 6 large lotus petals and 6 small, bounded by 3 incised circular decorative bands above and below; the centre medallion with a 7-petalled rosette bounded by 3 incised circular decorative bands; the outside wall plain; the neatly carved foot unglazed,

with a sand-coloured biscuit and distinct pontil scar,

D. 29 cm.

The University of Singapore

For a similar décor see *Locsin,* pl. 166, on a ring-handled bottle. See also nos. 298 and 304.

294 Bowl

The cavetto decorated with a motive similar to that of nos. 289, 290 and 291, between 4 incised circular decorative bands above and below; the centre medallion with a neatly carved lotus blossom inside 4 incised circular bands; with 4 incised circular decorative bands on the under side of the flattened lip, the outside wall with gouged vertical striations and another set of 5 incised circular bands on the lower body, below the pronounced keel; covered in a sea-green celadon glaze within, transmuted to a delightful deep duck-egg blue-green without; the carved foot unglazed, with a salmon-pink biscuit, lighter in tone within the pontil scar,

D. 21.1 cm.

The University of Singapore

For a similar centre medallion cf. *Locsin,* pl. 163.

295 Bowl

With steep sides, of lotus pod *(lien tzŭ)* shape; the cavetto with two sets of 3 incised circular decorative bands, the centre medallion with 2 similar bands; the outside wall plain; covered in a dark-green celadon glaze, somewhat abraded over the yellowish body, and with a fine crackle; the lower body and carved foot unglazed, with a dark rust-coloured biscuit, speckled with minute whitish particles, and with a distinct pontil scar,

D. 19 cm.

The University of Singapore

296 Dish

With curved sides; the small centre medallion slightly sunk; the outside lip and the lower body each with 3 carved circular mouldings; covered in a pale blue-green celadon glaze with a regular radial crackle; the carved foot unglazed, with a terracotta biscuit that is lighter in tone within the pontil scar,

D. 24 cm.

Dr. D. Stevens

297 Stem-dish or tazza

On a wide, splayed, and moulded foot; the upper cavetto decorated similarly to nos. 289, 290, 291 and 294; the centre medallion with a *cakra* or solar whorl bounded by 2 incised circular decorative bands; the outside wall with lightly-gouged vertical striations between 2 pairs of incised circular decorative bands and the lower part of the moulded foot with about 12 similar bands; covered in a sea-green celadon glaze; the hollow interior of the foot unglazed, with a bright pink biscuit, beige-coloured inside the pontil mark,

D. 25.4 cm.

The University of Singapore

The bowl and foot were separately thrown, as in most if not all of this type. The vessel was jammed down tight on the top of the pontil, and must have been more stable in the kiln than other vessels so fired   Most stem-dishes, however, show a natural tendency for the bowl part to subside downwards over the stem.

298 Stem-dish or tazza

Of a similar shape, but taller in proportion; the cavetto and centre medallion with a décor similar to that of no. 293, the outside wall with 3 incised circular decorative bands above and 4 below; the lower part of the moulded foot similarly decorated; all covered in a thin olive-green celadon glaze; the hollow interior of the foot unglazed, with a buff-coloured biscuit and pontil scar,

D. 21.4 cm.

The University of Singapore

299 Stem-dish or tazza

The bowl flattened, with everted lip and straight sides, and with a distinct keel between the outside wall and lower body; the centre medallion with a carved (or perhaps moulded) floral scroll; all covered in a glassy sea-green celadon glaze with a wide brown-veined crackle of *kuan yao* type; the interior of the foot with a pink biscuit, apparently stained black, and the broken end of the pontil jammed into the hollow stem,

D. 26.3 cm.

Mr. and Mrs. E. M. T. Lu

300 Vase

Of *yü hu chun p'ing* shape and with a cup-shaped mouth; the body moulded into 9 flat vertical panels below a short tubular neck; covered in a lustrous sea-green celadon glaze; the carved foot unglazed, with a light grey-brown biscuit and distinct pontil mark,

Ht 22.4 cm.

The University of Singapore

301 Vase

Of squat *yü hu chun p'ing* shape, and flared mouth; the neck with 2 incised circular decorative bands, and the body with 2 pairs of smaller bands between which is a pattern of doubled cross-hatched incised lines; covered in a finely-crackled olive-green celadon glaze; the carved foot unglazed, with a grey-brown biscuit and a distinct pontil scar,

Ht 17.6 cm.

Mr. S. R. Parker

For a similar vase cf. *Spinks II,* fig. 16 (Phya Buranasiri Bongsa).

302 Covered potiche

With high shoulder and sloping sides; the lid with a plain knop-handle and with two sets of 3 incised circular decorative bands on the dome; the shoulder with similar decorative bands between which is a register of short downward-pointing lotus leaves; covered in a grey-green celadon glaze; the lower body and foot unglazed, and with a brownish-grey biscuit; the foot uncarved, its outer side splayed outwards; the base flat, and with a pontil scar,

Ht 19 cm.

The University of Singapore

The foot is unique among the present collection; for an illustration see p. 193, lower left.

303 Covered potiche

With a short vertical neck and bulbous body; the domed cover with a plain (lotus bud) knop-handle, and with a register of incised saw-tooth pattern between 2 pairs of incised circular decorative bands on the dome; the body with several series of incised circular decorative bands; covered in a thin pale apple-green celadon glaze; the splayed foot similar to that of no. 302 but with a carved footrim; the foot unglazed, with a pale orange-pink biscuit and pontil scar,

Ht (with lid) 22.2 cm.

The University of Singapore

For a similar piece cf. *Spinks II,* fig. 18, above, right (Ladejinsky).

304 Part of a bowl

In profile like a swan's neck, and with a strongly-everted rim; the cavetto with the design shown by nos. 293 and 298; the centre medallion with a solar whorl (or *cakra*); the outside wall with combed lines representing lotus leaves; covered in a glassy crackled, sea-green celadon glaze; the inner side of the footrim and base unglazed, and with a pale orange-pink biscuit; the pontil scar with part of the pontil adhering,

Ht 7.6 cm.

The University of Malaya

Obtained at Amphoe Mueng, Sawankoloke.

305 Part of a bowl

With everted rim; the interior with an incised design similar to that shown by nos. 282, 289, 290, 291 and 294; the outside wall with gouged vertical flutings; all covered in a pale blue-grey celadon glaze; the carved foot unglazed and with

a grey biscuit, somewhat darker inside the distinct pontil mark,

D. 15.2 cm.

The University of Malaya

Obtained at Amphoe Mueng, Sawankoloke.

306 Part of a bowl

The interior with an incised design similar to that of no. 305; the mouthrim thickened; the outside wall with a pattern of gouged vertical flutings, emphasised above by incisions and representing lotus leaves; covered in a surprisingly intense sky-blue celadon glaze; the carved foot with an ochre-coloured biscuit and clear pontil scar,

D. 10.8 cm.

The University of Singapore

Obtained at Amphoe Mueng, Sawankoloke.

307 Part of a small bowl

The interior plain, the outside wall with gouged vertical flutings; covered in a crackled sea-green celadon glaze, of an olive tint in the interior; the carved foot with a salmon-pink biscuit,

D. 9 cm.

The University of Singapore

Purchased at Ban Ko Noi.

308 Bowl

Of similar shape to no. 306 and with the same intense blue celadon glaze; the cavetto with 3 incised circular decorative bands below the mouthrim, the centre medallion marked by one circular decorative band; the outside wall with gouged vertical flutings; the lower body and carved foot unglazed and with an iron-brown biscuit, lighter within the pontil mark,

D. 12.2 cm.

Mr. J. M. van Baak

309 Bowl

With everted and thickened mouthrim; the interior plain, the outside wall with emphatically gouged vertical flutings; covered in a glassy, crackled sea-green celadon glaze, abraded at the edges of the ribs and on the rim; the roughly carved foot with a brick-red biscuit and pontil scar,

D. 14.7 cm.

Mr. William Willetts

310 Bowl

With the same décor as no. 308; the mouthrim thickened, the outside wall below with lightly-gouged vertical flutings; covered in a limpid blue-green celadon glaze with a lustrous, sooty texture and of an olive tinge in the interior; the carved foot unglazed and with a brick-red biscuit,

D. 11.4 cm.

The University of Singapore

311 Bowl

With a profile similar to that of no. 304; the inside plain; the outside with a pattern of delicately gouged vertical flutings below the everted lip; the carved foot with a tall footrim, flared outwards above, and bevelled inwards below; the foot unglazed, with a grey biscuit flashed to a rusty red on parts of the outer side of the footrim, and with a distinct pontil scar,

D. 10.8 cm.

The University of Singapore

For an illustration of the foot see p. 193, lower right.

312 Bowl

Similar in shape and decoration to no. 307; covered in a glassy, crackled, sea-green celadon glaze; the lower body and carved foot unglazed and with a pale salmon-pink biscuit, lighter in tone inside the distinct pontil scar,

D. 10.1 cm.

Dr. D. Stephens

313 Bowl

With thickened mouthrim; plain, and covered in a glassy bottle-green celadon glaze with a fine crackle, eroded on the mouthrim, and running in tear-drops on the outside wall; the lower body and roughly-carved foot unglazed and with a bright canary-yellow biscuit, with reddish flushes,

D. 11.2 cm.

Mr. and Mrs. Frank Lammers

314 Bowl

Of lotus pod (lien tzŭ) shape; plain, and covered in a crackled grey-green celadon glaze; the outer side of the carefully-carved footrim splayed outwards; the foot with a greyish-brown biscuit, paler inside the pontil scar,

D. 10.1 cm.

The University of Singapore

Cf. *Spinks I*, fig. 54, right (Djakarta), from southern Sumatra.

315 Bottle

Of globular form, but without ring handles; the gouged decoration similar to that of no. 274; covered in a blue-green celadon glaze run thin on the ribs between the striations, and with a large dark-veined crackle; the lower body and carved foot unglazed, with a peat-coloured biscuit and distinct pontil scar,

Ht 13.9 cm.

The University of Malaya

With traces of a wood-ash glaze on the biscuit, outside the pontil scar.

316 Ring-handled bottle

Of small size; the shoulder and lower body with strongly gouged vertical striations arranged as in nos. 274 and 315; covered in a pale duck-egg blue celadon glaze, partly crackled; the lower body and foot unglazed, and with a reddish-brown biscuit; the foot flat, without a footrim,

Ht 10 cm.

The University of Singapore

317 Ring-handled bottle

Of tall proportions, the body gradually swelling outwards from the high narrow shoulder to a point an inch or so above the foot; the body decorated with strongly gouged flutings, cut slightly off the vertical, between two pairs of carved circular decorative bands; covered in a clear grey-green celadon glaze, somewhat speckled and finely crackled; the carved foot with a faded rose-coloured biscuit,

Ht 17.7 cm.

The University of Singapore

Cf. *Dublin*, no. 139 and *Spinks I*, fig. 46, left (Djakarta), from Acheh. No. 317 has tremendous character.

318 Ring-handled bottle

Of narrow proportions, the body ovoid; with 3 carved decorative circular bands on the upper shoulder; the body with gouged vertical fluting; covered in a matt pale sea-green celadon glaze; the lower body and carved foot unglazed and with a brick-red biscuit,

Ht 14.3 cm.

The University of Singapore

For the type cf. *Spinks I*, fig. 42, right (Djakarta), from north Sumatra.

319 Ring-handled bottle

Similar to nos. 317 and 318 but the body with straighter sides; the décor similar to that of no. 318; covered in an extremely glassy, crackled, dark-green celadon glaze that has run in tear-drops down each of the striations; the lower third of the body and the carved foot unglazed, and with a rough-textured reddish-brown biscuit,

Ht 15.2 cm.

The University of Singapore

320 Ring-handled bottle

Of barrel-shape and squat in comparison with nos. 317, 318 and 319, but similarly decorated; covered in a crackled grey-green celadon glaze that has run in tear-drops on the lower body; the carved foot with a powdery pale greyish-pink biscuit; the mouthrim built up,

Ht 9.8 cm.

Mr. William Willetts

321 Ring-handled bottle

Of similar form to no. 320 but slightly smaller; covered in a partly decayed pale grey-green celadon glaze; the lower body and carved foot with a bright brick-red biscuit,

Ht 9.3 cm.

Dr. D. Stevens

322 Ring-handled bottle

In general form similar to no. 319 but slighter, and strictly similar to no. 238 (with a caramel-coloured glaze); with a spiral incision revolving 11 times around the upper part of the vessel; covered in a sea-green celadon glaze with a minute white-veined crackle; the footrim markedly splayed outwards; the lower body and carved foot unglazed and with a light-brown biscuit,

Ht 11.7 cm.

Dr. D. Stevens

For a similar bottle with the same subtle *galbe* cf. *Spinks II*, below, right (Frasché).

323 Ring-handled bottle

Similar to no. 319 but the body more rounded; covered in a dark-green celadon glaze having a yellowish cast due to the veining of its minute crackle; the outer side of the footrim splayed outwards above and inwards below; the lower body and foot unglazed and with a light-brown biscuit,

Ht 11.7 cm.

The University of Singapore

324 Ring-handled bottle

Squat, and of globular form; the shoulder decorated with 6 incised circular decorative bands; the body covered in a glassy bottle-green celadon glaze, minutely crackled, and overhanging the lower body; the latter and the carved foot unglazed, and with a buff biscuit having pink flushes,

Ht 9.5 cm.

Mr. S. R. Parker

325   Ring-handled jar

Of globular form; covered in a pale-blue celadon glaze with mauve flushes and a wide, dark-veined crackle; the lower body and foot unglazed, with a warm buff-coloured biscuit; the tall button-like foot uncarved and with a flat base,

Ht 7.6 cm.

The University of Singapore

326   Sherd

Part of a globular ring-handled bottle in form similar to no. 247; with a deep grey-green celadon glaze,

D. (of mouth) 4.3 cm.

The University of Singapore

Collected at Ban Ko Noi in 1965. The relative thinness of the wall will be noted.

327   Sherd

Similar to no. 326, but with incised circular decorative bands on the upper shoulder; covered in a pale grey-green celadon glaze with brown flecks,

D. (of mouth) 4.3 cm.

The University of Singapore

Collected at the site; note the similarity of the mouthrim to that of no. 317.

328   Ring-handled jar

Of flattened globular form, the width of the body at its equator (7.1 cm.) being greater than its height; covered in a glassy grey-green crackled celadon glaze; the lower body and foot similar to that of no. 325 and with a similar biscuit,

Ht 6.8 cm.

The University of Singapore

329   Ring-handled jar

Similar to no. 328 in all respects, but with one decorative carved circular band on the shoulder, and with a matt, pale blue-green celadon glaze,

Ht 7 cm.

The University of Singapore

330   Ring-handled jarlet

With a long drooping shoulder, the turning-point being low down on the body-wall; the upper body with gouged vertical striations; covered in a blue-green celadon glaze; the lower body and flat, uncarved foot with a dense, bright-red biscuit with iron-black splashes,

Ht 7.3 cm.

The University of Singapore

331   Jarlet

In form similar to nos. 328, 329, and 330, but smaller, and with roughly gouged vertical striations; the body with a blue-green celadon glaze; the lower body and flat foot unglazed and with a red-brown biscuit,

Ht 6.3 cm.

The University of Singapore

Bought at Ban Ko Noi.

332   Ring-handled jarlet

Similar to no. 330, but with straight sides; the upper body, with roughly gouged vertical striations, covered with a grey-green celadon glaze; the lower body and tall, flat foot unglazed, and with a greyish-pink biscuit,

Ht 6.2 cm.

The University of Singapore

333   Miniature gourd-shaped vessel

With ring-handles, and with 3 decorative incised circular bands below the mouthrim and 4 more on the shoulder; covered in a lifeless pale-green celadon glaze; the lower body and carved foot unglazed and with a brownish-red biscuit,

Ht 8.7 cm.

The University of Singapore

For one similar cf. *Spinks I*, fig. 45, right (Djakarta), from the Celebes.

334   Oil jar

Of flattened globular form and with a short tubular conical neck; the shoulder with about 8 incised circular decorative bands in a continuous spiral; covered in a sea-green celadon glaze; the carved foot unglazed, with a salmon-pink biscuit and some black adhesions,

Ht 4.1 cm.

Dr. D. Stevens

335 Oil jar

Of flattened globular shape, the wide shoulder being almost flat, and with a short tubular neck; the shoulder, with an incised solar whorl or *cakra*, separated from the body by two horizontal circular mouldings; covered in a matt grey-green celadon glaze; the lower body and carved foot unglazed, and with a burnt-brick-coloured biscuit,

Ht 3.8 cm.

Dr. D. Stevens

For this type cf. *Spinks II*, pl. 17, top, right (Frasché).

336 Kendi

Of flattened globular form, completely enclosed above by a domed top, with a short conical spout and 3 ring-handles; the dome with 7 incised circular decorative bands in a continuous spiral, the shoulder with 5 similar bands; covered in a crackled drab sea-green celadon glaze; the lower body and carved foot unglazed, and with a rust-brown biscuit,

D. 10.5 cm.

The Sinclair Collection

337 Kendi

In the form of a crested bird with raised and recurved crescent-shaped tail; the open mouth functional; the body lightly incised with wing-feathers and with a quatrefoil on the breast; the tall, bowed neck perhaps luted onto the body; all covered in a crackled olive-green celadon glaze; the carved foot with a putty-coloured biscuit; the head and tail of the bird and the mouthrim repaired,

Ht 12 cm.

Mr. K. T. Goh

338 Kendi

The spout modelled as head and neck of the male Mandarin duck, the open mouth functional; the vessel's mouth strongly flared and with a flat lip; the bowed neck with vertical flutings, and perhaps luted onto the body; the body globular, with a wreath of lotus leaves incised on the shoulder, a peony scroll with 2 blooms on the body, and a register of vertical flutings on the lower body; covered in a blue-green celadon glaze shading to olive-green above; the inner side of the carved foot and the base unglazed and with a buff-coloured biscuit, lighter in tone within the distinct pontil scar,

Ht 16.4 cm.

Mr. K. T. Goh

For a similar vessel cf. *Spinks I*, fig. 38, right (Djakarta), described as a narghili bottle and said to have come from Acheh.

339 Kendi

The spout modelled as the head and neck of the sacred goose *(hamsa)*, its open mouth functional; the tail of the bird erect and crescentic; the mouth of the vessel cup-shaped, the neck bowed and separated from the body by a powerful moulding; the globular body with incisions representing the bird's wings; the body covered with an irregular matt olive-green celadon glaze, parts of the neck having been undipped; the lower body and carved foot unglazed, and with a grey biscuit partly flashed brown; the base with a muddy-brown biscuit and the trace of a thin-walled pontil,

Ht (to top of crest) 18.7 cm.

The Sinclair Collection

340 Maternity figurine

Similar to no. 280 but the head missing, as also that of the child; covered in a dark olive-green celadon glaze; the foot unglazed, with a greyish-pink biscuit and kiln adhesions,

Ht 7 cm.

The University of Singapore

341 Maternity figure

The head missing; instead of a child the woman holds a fan to her prominent pelleted breasts; covered in a grey-green celadon glaze with iron-brown mottling; the foot unglazed and with a light-brown biscuit,

Ht 6.8 cm.

The University of Singapore

For an explanation of these two images cf. no. 280.

342 Offering dish

Of flattened form; covered with a granular and finely crackled sea-green celadon glaze with some black flecks on the everted mouthrim and upper cavetto; the inside medallion marked by a circular ridge; the inner side of the footrim and the base unglazed and with a burnt-red-brown biscuit, lighter inside the pontil scar,

D. 41.3 cm.

The University of Singapore

343 Offering dish

Of similar form to no. 342, but the cavetto decorated with delicately gouged radial flutings around the plain centre medallion; the lower outside wall with a moulded circular ridge; the inner side of the foot-rim and the base unglazed and with a brownish-pink biscuit, greyer in hue inside the pontil scar,

D. 41.3 cm.

The University of Singapore

Both dishes, considering their size, are superbly potted.

GROUP FIVE: SANKAMPAENG AND KALONG WARES

344 Sherd

Fragment of a dish with a double-moulded rim, the lower (inner) moulding wide and flat; decorated in underglaze iron-black, the rim with a scrolled design, and the centre medallion with a floral spray; the inside wall and the outside wall down

to the lower body covered with a thin glossy celadon glaze; the foot with a raised rim; the base flat, unglazed, and with a grey biscuit,

Max d. 25.2 cm.

The University of Singapore

Sankampaeng. For a similar complete dish cf. *Nimmana.*, pl. 3, left. No. 344 was collected by Nimmanahaeminda at the site in 1952.

345 Waster

Fragment of a dish with cavetto and centre medallion; decorated in underglaze iron-black, the centre medallion with 3 circular decorative bands within which are 2 summarily drawn fish facing in opposite directions and flanking a central bulls-eye; the glaze and biscuit similar to that of no. 344, as also the structure of the foot,

Max. d. 18.5 cm.

The University of Singapore

Sankampaeng. For similar dishes see *Nimmana.*, pls 9, left and right, and 10, left; cf. also *Indiana*, pl. 115 (Nimmana-haeminda). No. 345 has a fragment of a similar dish adhering to it, inverted, and resting on it rim to rim, so illustrating the method of firing first remarked by Nimmanahaeminda. Collected by Nim-manahaeminda at the site in 1952.

346 Waster

Distorted during firing, but physically almost complete; similar to no. 345 in form, style and subject of decoration, glaze, biscuit and structure of foot,

D. 21 cm.

The University of Singapore

Sankampaeng. Collected by Nimmana-haeminda at the site in 1952.

347 Jar

With a wide flaring mouth and a double S-shaped profile; decorated with a single moulded circular rib at the junction of neck and shoulder, and covered in an irregular mottled chocolate glaze with some lighter brown flambé effects on the lower body; the plain flat foot exhibiting a coarse brown, mud-coloured biscuit,

Ht 12.3 cm.

The University of Singapore

Sankampaeng. Acquired by the writer at the site in 1965. For a similar shape cf. *Nimmana.*, pl. 21, right. It is also found in the Kalong repertory: cf. *Nimmana.*, pl. 28, right.

348 Utility jar

Of massive form; the mouth, with a broad flat top, is connected by the short neck to a shoulder with rounded profile continued down the length of the body to an exceptionally broad and substantial flat foot; the upper body with a dark olive-green celadon stoneware glaze; the lower body and foot with a dense greenish-brown biscuit,

Ht 20.3 cm.

The University of Malaya

Sankampaeng. This jar, which weighs 6¼ lbs. has the solidity of some sorts of European utility stonewares such as old-fashioned ginger-beer bottles, or storage jars for writing-ink, etc. The name was given by Nimmanahaeminda, who found no. 348 at the site in 1952. For a similar example cf. *Nimmana.*, pl. 15, right. The shape can also be found in the Kalong repertory: cf. *Nimmana.*, pl. 25, left. For an illustration of the foot see p. 194, upper right.

349 Part of a bottle

Of *yü hu ch'un p'ing* shape, but with the flared upper part of the neck broken; covered in a thin greyish celadon glaze; the foot with a flat base displaying an orange-coloured biscuit,

Present ht 14.4 cm.

The University of Singapore

Sankampaeng. These bottles were made by the hundreds, but an unbroken one is a rarity. Cf. *Nimmana.*, pl. 16, right.

350 Tall jar

With four ring-handles and a moulded rib separating shoulder from neck; the

mouthrim everted; the upper body covered in a mottled chocolate-brown glaze, the lower body and wide flat foot unglazed and sharing a fine, dense, grey biscuit,

Ht 33.6 cm.

The University of Singapore

Sankampaeng. The aspect of the foot, so similar to that of no. 348, as well as other features displayed by this pot, including a shoulder moulding similar to that of no. 347, make the attribution to Sankampaeng virtually certain. From Indonesia. A similar jar is illustrated in *Spinks I*, fig. 51, right (Djakarta), from north central Java, stated to be 'possibly of Sukhothai origin'. Another practically identical in form to no. 350 is shown in *Fox*, pl. 135, from Calatagan, and is ascribed to Kalong. For an illustration of the foot see p. 194, lower left.

351 Sherd

Fragment of a dish with a flattened rim; somewhat thinly potted, and decorated in underglaze iron-black on a creamy-white slip overlying a light-grey body,

Max. l. 8.5 cm.

Mr. K. T. Goh

Kalong. For a complete example featuring the motive visible on no. 351 cf. *Nimmana.*, pl. 24, left and right, and pl. 26, right.

352 Sherd

Part of a dish; thinly potted and decorated in underglaze iron-black directly on the body, with radial petal-like brush-strokes on the cavetto, and a petal rosette on the centre medallion; the glaze with a fine whitish crackle; the foot with a raised rim not dissimilar to the Sankampaeng examples, nos. 344, 345 and 346, and showing a buff-coloured biscuit,

Max. d. of foot 12.2 cm.

Mr. K. T. Goh

Kalong. A complete example of this type of dish appears in *Nimmana.*, pl. 23, right.

124

162

222

250

238

275

2

3

4

5

6

7

8

9

10

11

13

12

14

15

16

17

18

19

20

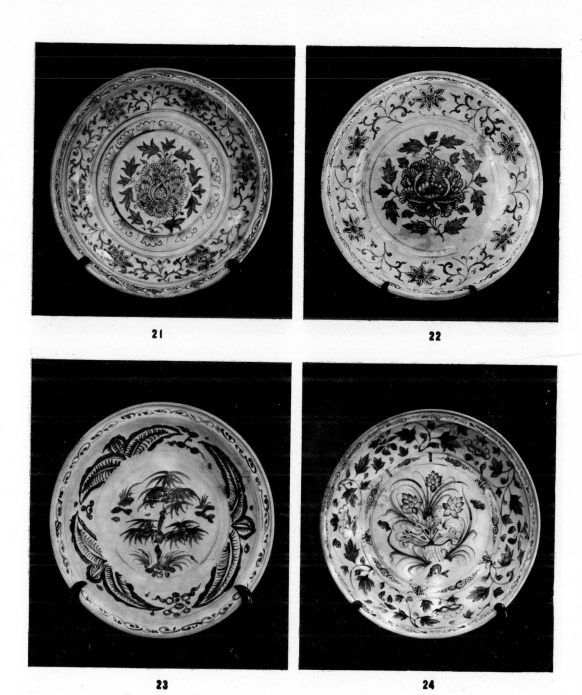

21

22

23

24

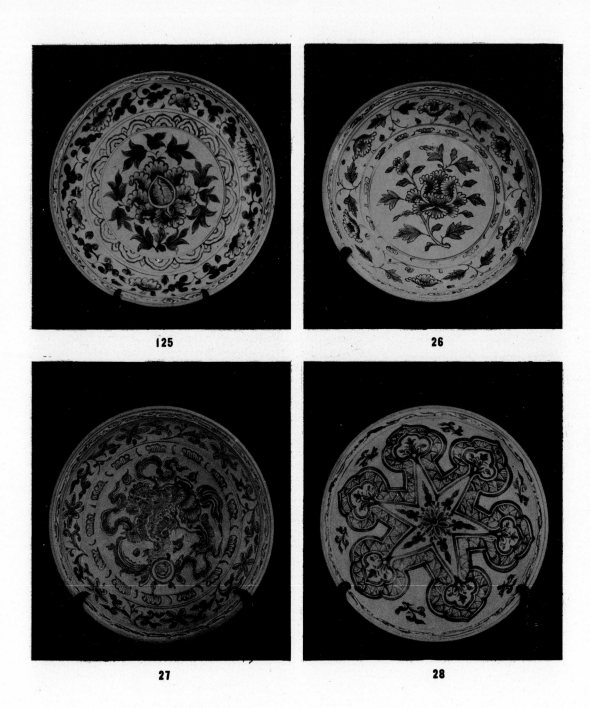

125

26

27

28

29

30

31

32

33

34

36

35

37

38

39

40

43

42

41

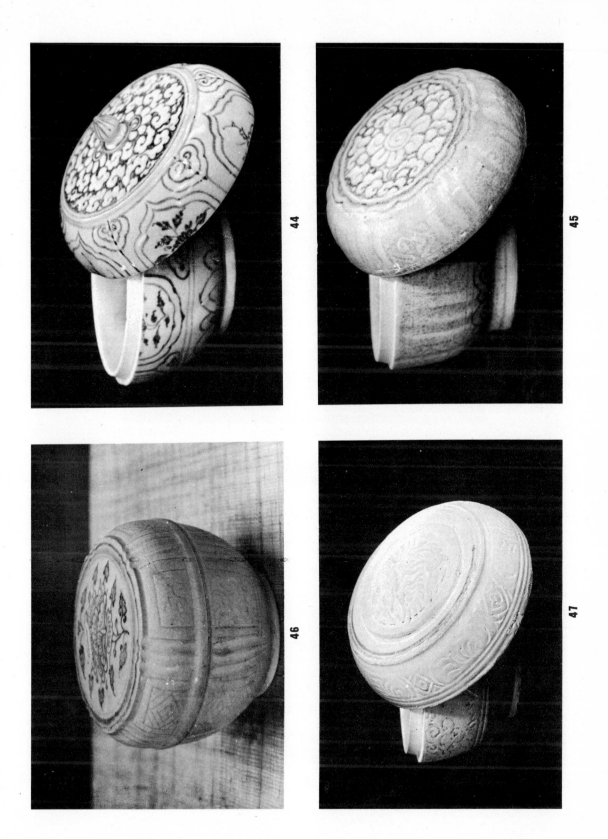

44

45

46

47

48

49

50

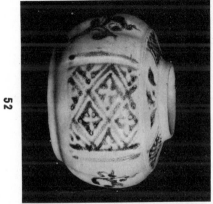

52

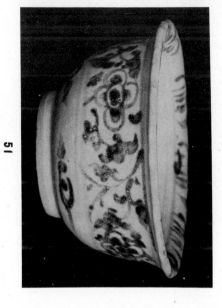

51

53

54

55

56

57

59

58

60

61

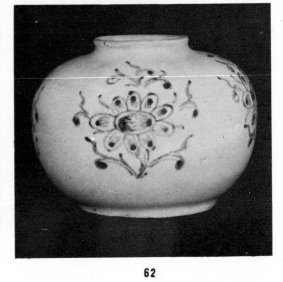

62

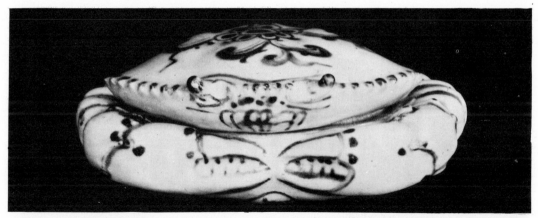

63

64   65   64

166

67

68

69

70

71

72

73

75

76

74

77

78

80

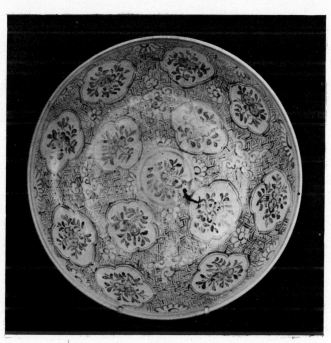

79

81

82

83

84

86

87

88

89 a

89 b

90

91

92

93

94

95

96

97

98

99

100

101

103

102

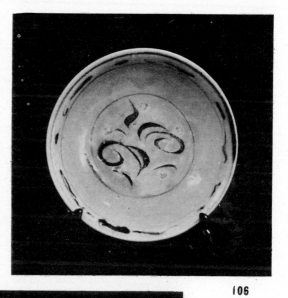

106

105

104

119

107

108

109

110

111

112

113

114

115

116

117

119

118

120

121

123

128

127

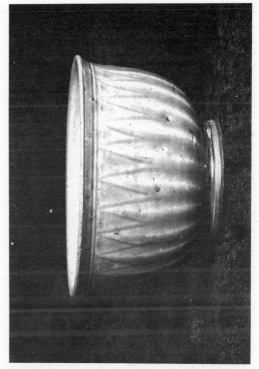

129

124

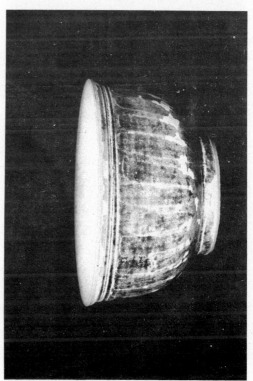

125

126

130

133

132

131   122

134

135

136

139

141

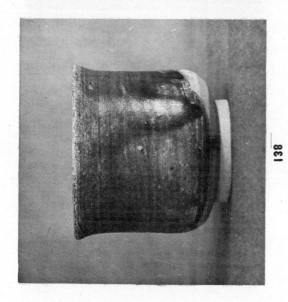

138

140

142

144

143

145

146

147

148

149

150

151

153

152

154

155

156

157

158

159

160

161

163

164

166

165

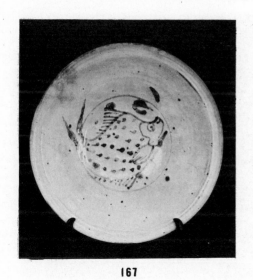

167

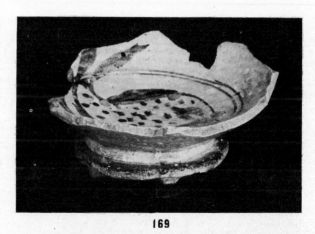

169

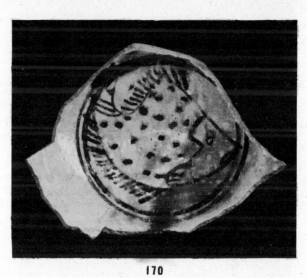

170

168

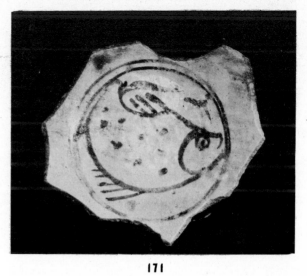

171

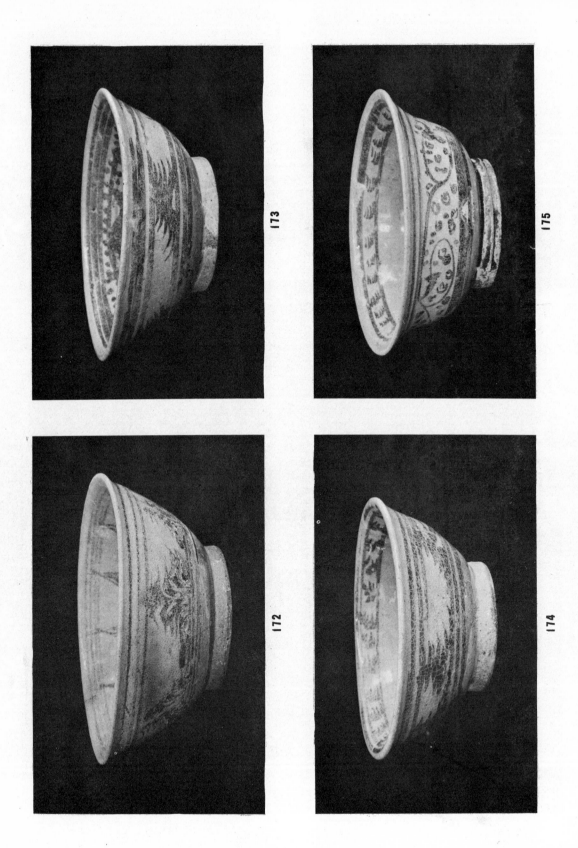

173

175

172

174

176

177

178

179

180

181

182

183

184

185

186

187

188

189

190

191

192

193

194

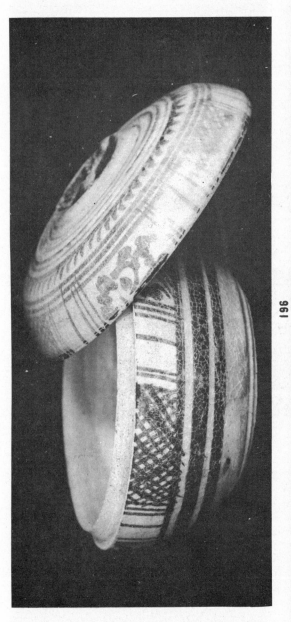

196

195

144

198

197

199

200

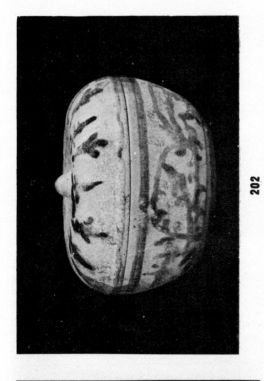

202

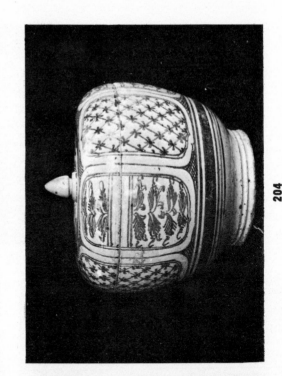

204

201

203

206

208

205

207

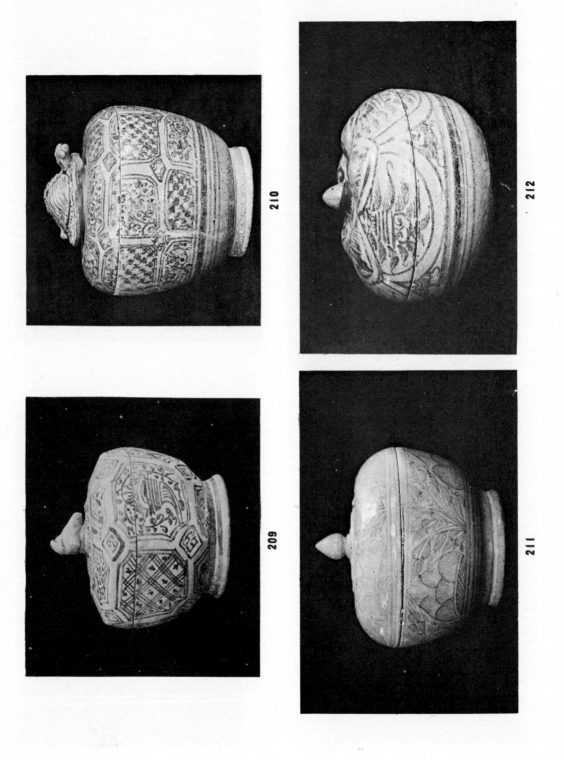

209

210

211

212

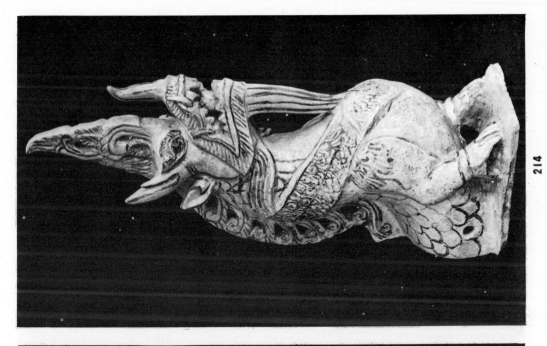

214

213

149

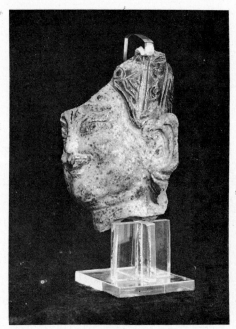

215   216

217

218

220

221

219

222

223

224

225   **226**

228

230

227

229

231

232

233

235

234

236

237

239

240

241

242

243

245

244

246

247

248

249

251

252

253

254

255

256

257

258

259

260

262

261

263

264

265

266

267

268

269

270

271

272

273

274

276

277

279

278

280

281

282

283

284

285

286

287

288

289

290

291

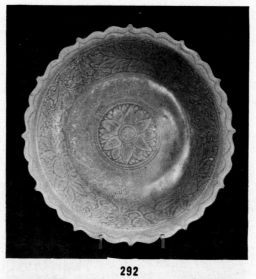

292

293

294

295

296

297

298

299

300

301

303

302

305

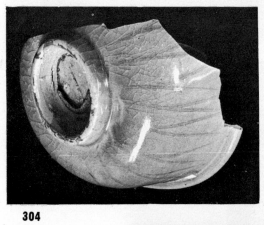

304

306

307

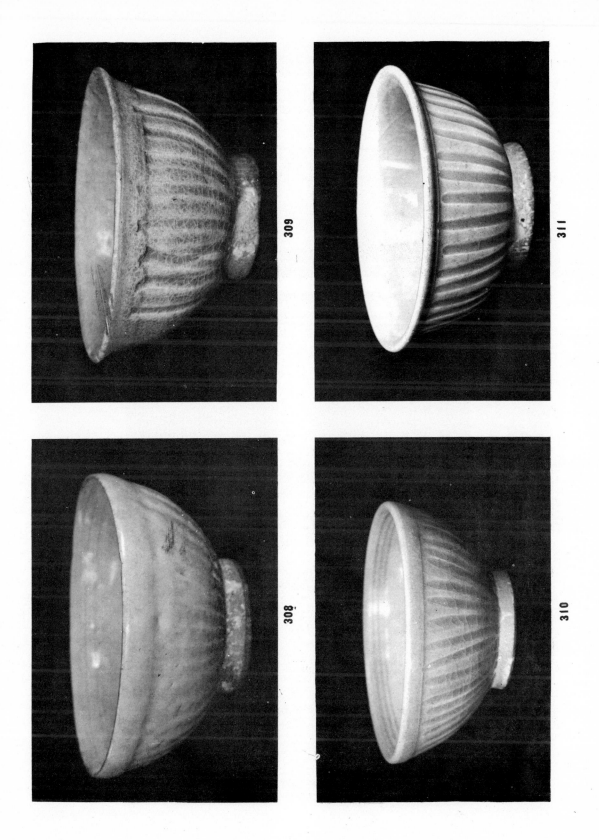

309

311

308

310

312

313

314

315

316

317

318

319

320

321

322

323

324

325

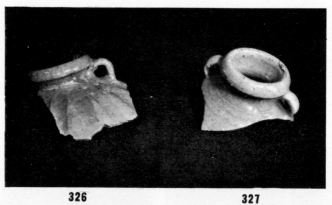

326   327

328   329

330   331   332

333

334

335

336

337

338

339

340

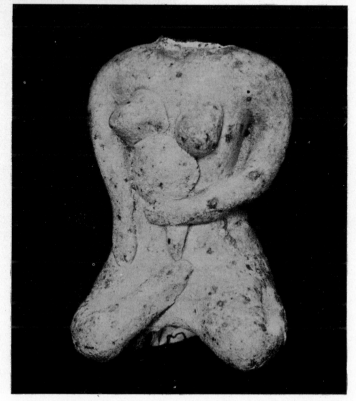

341

185

342

343

344

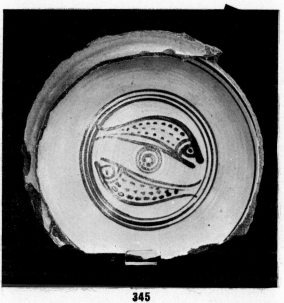

345

346

348

350

347

349

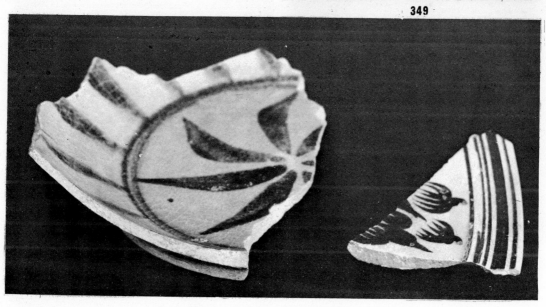

352   351

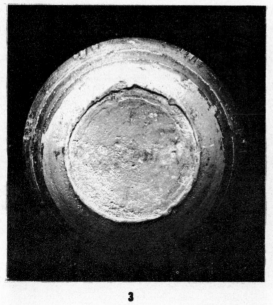

3

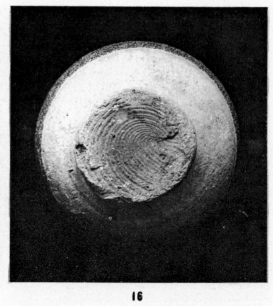

16

25

28

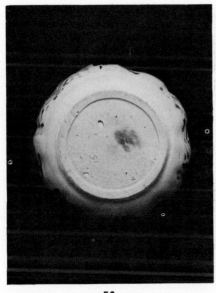

52

126

160

168

172

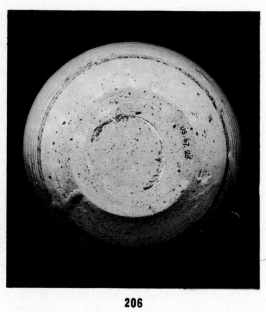

206

212

240

282

291

302

311

348

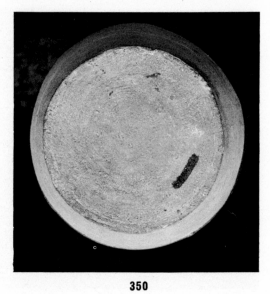

350

346